A Joyous Christmas,
to you, and New Bl____
in the com____

____ Geary

12.25.56

THE LAST PASSENGER

THE LAST PASSENGER

By JAMES RALPH JOHNSON

THE MACMILLAN COMPANY · NEW YORK · 1956

Library of Congress catalog card number: 56–10394

To Betty Ann and Vera Sue

Foreword

According to the records, the last passenger pigeon died in the Cincinnati Zoo in 1914. I like to think that the real last passenger never saw a zoo. He lived in a world populated with many birds now extinct or nearly so. This is his story.

Contents

THE NEST ON THE OHIO

NESTS ON THE OHIO

AT DAWN an icy mist flooded the forest and hugged the surface of the Ohio River. The cold was a thing alive, seeping into the thousands of loose-stick nests of passenger pigeons built in the forks of the gray oaks and gaunt sycamores that huddled together in the bottom land.

The setting passengers fluffed their belly feathers to protect their unborn. They blinked red eyes in the wind that spilled over the limestone cliffs across the river and scampered down the valley, slapping muddy waters white, and twisting a reckless path through the shuddering trees.

The one-inch layer of white pasted on the limbs of the trees was not snow. It was too cold to snow. The passengers had been in this nesting area for days now, depositing layer upon layer of guano on tree limbs and on the ground below the nests. The layers were so thick that the early spring rains failed to loosen them. Only when ice and frost cracked the plastered droppings did the rains loosen them and carry them to the ground—where, after a few years, the plants beneath the understory would thrive on the richness.

There were many broken nests on the ground, knocked from splintered limbs by the stones and bullets of the market hunters who had been here, following the huge flock from Michigan.

The winter wind failed to carry the odor of the pigeons from the forest. The dead squabs that the market hunters had missed among the leaves, and the distorted strings of pigeon intestines flung onto the creek banks by men cleaning their kills, generated an overbearing stench that caused much of the nervousness in the tense bodies of the setting passengers.

But the main reason for the alertness of the birds and for the nervous twisting of their heads was in the redbud thickets in the flat toward town. A man stood there blowing cloudy breaths into the air. His faded blue Union Army blouse, tattered since Gettysburg, was pulled tight around his neck. He grumbled to himself.

The passengers made no sound. The man had been here before with the others, shooting the birds that showed themselves against the sky. The instinct to restore their kind was stronger than the instinct for self-preservation. The shooting had not been heavy enough to drive the flock to a new nesting area.

The passengers waited.

The man stood for a while, searching the trees with eyes slitted against the cold. The nests were too scattered now. It would take at least one shot for each pigeon. He could not make enough money that way. This was a far cry from last week, when one shotgun blast blew a half-dozen nests from the trees. He muttered aloud and turned back toward town, kicking angrily through the brittle leaves.

As he did so, a dozen gray-feathered balls flung themselves skyward with flailing wings beating out a warning. Then the air grew heavy with the thunder of thousands of startled birds. They formed into a long waving curtain of living pigeons. The sun, just sifting through the bare trees on the ridge to the east, glinted from the fluttering gray wings even as it flashed from the waves of the river.

But the commotion had no meaning for Blue, the un-hatched squab, for he was still pecking tediously away at the walls of his egg cell. The tiny squab faced toward the big end of the egg and the air space there. His bill was still too soft, too tender to break the shell; but over the past few days a hard egg tooth had developed on the upper bill to furnish the tool with which he worked. The egg tooth would disappear in a few days.

The mother bird had returned, and the sun had melted the mist with the cold, by the time Blue's bill poked through the first tiny opening. The fresh air rushed inside the egg, filling the young bird's lungs and giving him new energy. The air did not stop at his lungs, but was breathed into tiny tubes that extended to air sacs scattered throughout the bird's body wherever there was a space not filled by a vital organ. The bones were hollow too, and received the air, thus starting the aeration that was to allow the bird to lead a far more intensive life, at a much faster pace, than that of human beings.

The opening flaked larger rapidly, and Blue tumbled out on his face when the shell fell apart. The mother bird pecked at its fragments, a physical appetite urging her to replace the calcium in her body which had built the egg, and instinct warning her to get rid of the bits of shell so that they would not drop to the ground and show animals of prey that a defenseless young bird lay in the nest above.

The breeze streaming up through the wet stick nest plastered an icy breath against Blue's damp skin, and he reared high on ungainly legs to snuggle in among the soft fluff and hair feathers of the pigeon hen's breast. The mother bird was warm, well over a hundred degrees. Blue wormed his head up through the downy chest to her skin. The wet hair on his body dried into a fuzz in the heat radiating from her body, heat generated by her several hundred heartbeats a minute.

Because Blue's feet, hanging below the protecting feathers, grew cold, he stood on one foot at a time, drawing the other up into warmth. He found a solution by standing on the mother bird's hard feet, which cut off some of the cold from below.

When it grew stuffy underneath her body, he worked his head out through the stiff wing feathers. The sunlight glinting off the river swelled his red eyes, and he blinked uncertainly at the bottom-land forest. It looked big and hostile.

A faraway whistle made him jerk his head back. Seconds later he eased it out again, to see a side-wheeler river boat grinding upstream. It seemed out of place in the quiet forest land. The hickory and oak fueling its boilers gave off clouds of smoke, which boiled over the lips of its funnels and spread up the river.

To Blue, the smoke smelled rich and sweet. It was the first odor to make an impression on his sense of smell, which would never be particularly keen.

There was also a fascination in the long ribbons of

white water that curved gently outward from the bow of the boat, subtly changing the muddy water to streamers of flecked amber. As the craft warped around the bend, skidding its stern to the outside, the side-wheels spun a wake that looked like a long cotton blanket whose far end finally dissolved into the muddy waters a half-mile back.

Two men stood among the cotton bales stacked on the main deck of the boat. They appeared to be businessmen, perhaps from Cincinnati. Suddenly, as the river boat's pilot roared an oath, the craft caught her turning bow in a mud bar at the curve of the river. Though the side-wheels were reversed, the boat refused to back off. It would take a half-hour to work her free. One of the men called to the hunter walking the riverside path through the willows only a few yards away.

"How're the wood pigeons holding out?"

The hunter paused to pull out a bandanna and blow his nose.

"Plenty left. Too scattered to fool with."

"Heard about this nesting ground last week. The trees are covered with pigeon droppings for a couple of miles back."

"Yep. Goes on for four or five miles up the river. Pretty well cleaned out now, though. Six weeks ago, when the flock first settled in here, there must have been five hundred people getting the birds for market. We loaded up two boats with nothing but barreled pigeons down at the landing last week."

"How's the market holding at Louisville?"

"Still high as ever—up to ten cents a bird. They been

railroading the barrels out of Louisville to New York and Philadelphia. The restaurants there have been doing a big business lately, folks tell me."

"It's easy to see why. I had a couple of pigeons for dinner yesterday. A fat squab breast sure makes good eating. Wife's been canning a few."

"Yeah, folks around here have been canning a right smart, too. Hogs getting mighty fat. People been running their hogs down here in the river bottoms to eat the squabs that fall out of the nests. Hogs get fatter off them than they can off seed corn."

"Something I've never been able to figure," the talkative boat passenger said, "is how the pigeons find enough food to eat when they're so thick."

The hunter laughed and waved an arm around him.

"They clean out the woods. You won't find an acorn or beechnut or seed for fifty miles around here now, outside of right here under the nests. The pigeons have got them all. It's going to play havoc with next year's squirrel crop."

The hunter threw up his hand as a parting gesture and moved off down the trail, paying no attention to the *coos* of the scattered setting birds in the limbs overhead. Perhaps some other part of the nesting area would offer a thicker target of pigeons.

As the river boat worked her way free of the mud bar, the two men standing among the cotton bales continued to talk.

One said: "You know, I was reading an editorial in the Louisville paper. It was about this bird-man Audubon who used to live around here about fifty years ago. He left his house one morning to go to Louisville, nearly fifty miles away. Took him all day to get there, and he said that all day long the sky was full of pigeons moving along in a flock."

"Sounds like a tale," the other man replied.

"Yes, I guess it does. I'll bet this flock here would take a couple of hours to clear a point, though." He was silent for a moment before musing, "Guess we'll never be able to get rid of them."

"Nope. They're like flies. Always be around." The man lit his pipe and blew the smoke out in a heavy cloud before him. "These fool pigeons can sure stink up a stand of woods."

Chapter Two

THE WEASEL DID NOT SEE THE GREAT HORNED OWL

LIFE AND DEATH

Before Blue was completely dry the mother pigeon stood up and hopped to the edge of the nest. He stretched forward awkwardly to stay beneath her, trying to perch on her feet as she shifted.

She slipped her bill underneath Blue to shove him back into the open nest. Instinct pushed his opened bill up to receive the curd from the throat of the big bronze-breasted cock perched on the limb near the hen. The curd, a thickened cream of regurgitated food formed in the crops of both male and female, served as the milk to give strength to the newborn pigeons. This curd, or pigeon milk, and later acorns, would feed Blue until he could find his own food.

Blue slipped his bill into the throat of the parent bird and received the curd as the cock's throat muscles forced the food into Blue's mouth.

When the cock finished, he fluffed his feathers and took the hen's place on the nest. It was now mid morning, and the cock would warm Blue for the remainder of the day, until it was time for the hen to take over again. The parent birds had followed this procedure during the incubation period of over two weeks before the egg hatched.

Blue paid little attention to the change of warm cover. He quickly snuggled under the cock. The hen flew to the feeding grounds, miles away, to stuff herself with beech and acorn mast and wild seeds. She needed an ample surplus above her own food requirements, so that sufficient curd could be excreted from her crop for Blue's next meal.

As his matted feathers dried into a soft yellow blanket to cover his body, Blue stretched his ragged wings down to scratch their tips where the gently flowing blood made them tingle. After pushing around under the cock's body, he found a spot protected from drafts by the oak limb. He slept for a long time.

Those first days were uneventful, and Blue forgot them as they passed. They taught no lessons, but then he had no reason to know that there were things to be learned, and that they were the only days of security. Only the parents alternating on the nest disturbed him. He liked their comings and goings, though, because their arrivals meant that his crop would be filled.

Then there were long hours of sitting under one of the old birds, with his naked head poked out behind the parent's wing. In this manner Blue surveyed the surrounding forest patiently and in detail.

Once, after a change of parents on the nest, Blue watched the big bronze cock that had fathered him fly to the creek bank a few yards away. There were other pigeons there, and the cock joined them in bathing. It seemed a pleasant thing to do. The pigeons stood in the shallow water and sprayed it into the air with their wings as they fluttered. They explored the flight and covert feathers of the wings with their bills, and flipped water into the fluffed contour feathers on breasts and backs.

Bathing for the pigeons was vital. It prevented the mites and feather lice from obtaining a homestead. The passengers were particular in their choice of water. Whenever the eddies became muddied, the birds moved upstream to clear water.

After their baths the passengers hopped to rocks and fallen limbs, where they spent long minutes preening themselves. The pigeons brought their feathers back to a healthy gloss by squeezing oil from a preen gland on the rump with their beaks and working it out to the tips of their feathers.

Special care was used in repairing the split barbules that webbed the hairlike rays extending from the shaft of the feather. These webbed rays formed the blade-shaped feather. An occasional collision with a limb or a peck by a jealous cock broke the invisible barbules holding the rays together and split the feather blade to the shaft. Oil squeezed from the skin ducts repaired the barbules, and the feather blade was soon restored to its unbroken contour.

During the bathing the water carried off some of the pigeon bloom, or milt, which protected the feathers from moisture during flight. The milt, a chalky white powder, was preened back into the feather coat by busily working beaks.

Blue's hair feathers, or filoplumes, were soon intermixed with growing fluff feathers and stiffer contour feathers, but these later additions were still insignificant. The young pigeon still looked like the ungainly squab that first pecked its way from the egg. His legs were long and awkward; his head, with its oversized beak, was nearly as big as an adult's; and his wings were still only a framework for flight feathers to come.

As days passed, Blue's horizon broadened to take in the nests in other trees. The tops of the limbs had now become encrusted with a thicker layer of white droppings. He watched, fascinated, as the older squabs were pushed to the ground by their parents; he heard the angry squawks of the young who were left to shift for themselves. The parent birds left the nesting area as soon as their squabs were put on their own.

On the ground were snorting hairy pigs, which rooted among the bushes below the nesting trees, seeking out the defenseless squabs. Blue watched an old razorback sow and her litter of a dozen young ones clean out all the younger squabs from a half-acre of scrub oak. Only those squabs whose flight feathers had developed enough to allow them to flutter over logs and bushes escaped the charging little pigs, who pounced on their prey with happy squeals.

The beechnuts and acorns lying untouched by the parent passengers among the leaves were ignored by the pigs. The stored fat in the bodies of the squabs was much more of a delicacy than the strong oils of the nut meats.

The pigs fattened quickly on their diet. Once Blue saw several horse-drawn wagons creak up a road across the brook. After stopping, the men on the wagons turned dozens of young porkers free. Corn could be saved for next winter's feed.

The numbers of squabs killed by the rooting hogs were countless, but the numbers remaining were also countless. The passenger pigeons and their production of offspring seemed to have no end in this isolated valley of the Ohio.

On days when the sky was blue and only slightly spotted with fragments of high clouds, Blue's parents left for long intervals, feeding fifty miles away. When an overcast hid the blue and when low-floating nimbus clouds threatened rain, the parents flew only a short distance. Dark days were not to the passengers' liking. They were like harbingers of nightfall, when all pigeons deserted the open sky for their woodland roosts.

As a new crop of squabs fluttered on the ground, men with clubs and large burlap bags moved among them. They silenced the birds with quick blows and loaded their bags with dead. Some would be rendered into fat, as the Indians had done for centuries before the coming of the frontiersmen. Other squabs would fill the cooking pots of farm and town dwellers for miles around, and a few would be canned for shipment to New York and Washington and Boston.

A few days of warm weather hastened the annual molting of the parents. Old feathers were shed from their bodies, and the process of replenishment that would provide mature new feathers in about three months was begun. The molting period strained the physical capacity of the pigeons, and they tired from short flights. The birds hunted rich, oily foods such as grains and greens that could be easily digested. Under this diet, the molt followed its regular cycle of, first, primary flight feathers, and then the tail and body feathers, each falling out as the replacing feather grew halfway to maturity.

One day Blue's parents left and did not return. As evening approached and no one came to feed him, he set up a steady squawk until another hen settled on the nest and began to stuff him. Though he had never seen the ragged hen, it made no difference to him.

The foster mother was following an occasional pattern of passenger pigeons. Orphan squabs of a flock were sometimes adopted by foster parents and taken care of until they were able to obtain their own food.

The next day the foster mother filled his crop and continued to stuff the food mast in as he swallowed halfheartedly. Over a period of two days she forced him so full of food that his crop equaled the size of his young body. On the third day, without warning, she suddenly shoved a foot under Blue and flipped him from the nest.

Blue left it upside down; but something told him that this was wrong, and he struggled upright to beat the air with inadequate wings that barely slowed his descent. The leaf layer on the ground broke his fall.

The world seemed very large from the ground. The nest, drafty as it was, had been comparatively cozy and protected. A freak late spring snow had sifted two inches of white onto the leaf mold. Blue sat motionless for a while, staring at a nearby older squab who scratched the snow and oak leaves aside to get at the seeds and grubs.

The squab worked past, showering Blue with snow.

The younger bird blinked his red eyes excitedly until the snow melted from his head.

From somewhere up the creek a great horned owl hooted its displeasure at the gathering thunderstorm that hid the setting sun. A pig's squeal sounded from the redbud thicket on the creek. Instinct moved Blue to pitch forward on his huge crop and push himself along with his feet until he reached a clump of dead broom sedge in a clearing. Inside, he found protection and a dry spot, and he shifted around like a dog settling for a nap until he made himself comfortable. Although it would be an hour until darkness, Blue had no desire to take advantage of the daylight. Because he was not hungry, he felt no need to move from his refuge.

It was well that he didn't. Blue watched a cotton rat spring from under a log to kill a squab a few feet away. One bite on the defenseless squab's head crumpled it. The rat, already fattened by a steady diet of squabs, ripped the dead bird apart, jerking his head from side to side to tear the soft muscles from bones. The hot flesh steamed in the cold air.

A movement across a creek attracted Blue's attention. A handsome black-and-white bird, a loggerhead shrike, pitched forward from a honey locust tree and flew toward the rat. Its odd bounding flight carried it swiftly near the water, over the ash saplings on the banks, and to the ground beside the rat.

The rat turned to defend itself, but the shrike buried its black bill in the loose shoulder skin of the animal. The surprised rodent forgot its kill and threshed free, squealing in pain and snapping savagely.

Bouncing back into the air, the shrike came down on top of the rat, its sharp bill this time boring into the animal's skull. The rat crumpled as quickly as the squab had a moment earlier. The shrike sat astride the rat to survey its prey. Its alert black eyes, set in a black raccoon-like mask, watched to see if further effort were needed. It wasn't.

Blue watched the shrike attempt to fly with the rat in its bill, but the weight of the animal was too great. The bird then tried to eat the rat, holding it with its feet; but its pecks were so voracious that it could not maintain its balance, for its claws had not the strength to grasp like the talons of a hawk. The shrike glanced about, with quick jerking head, until it spied a honey locust bush a short distance away. The bird jerked the rat toward the bush, excitedly jumping over its prey and flitting about in an attempt to find a better way to drag the animal.

At the tree the shrike pulled the rat a foot off the ground to a locust thorn. With a quick thrust the animal was impaled on the sharp hanger. The shrike again surveyed the situation, and patiently worked the rat farther onto its hook until the thorn protruded from the opposite side of the rodent's neck.

This done, the shrike began to eat. First the skin on the animal's head was pecked off. Then the sharp bill shattered the skull, and the rat's brains were eaten. The hind legs formed the next delicacy on the shrike's menu. Twenty or so billfuls of hair were pulled from the legs. With vigorous swipes of its head, much like the rat's efforts to dismember the squab, the shrike ripped off the skin; then the muscles were skillfully clipped out and eaten.

This seemed to satisfy the shrike's hunger, for it stopped eating and sat in the top of the locust bush for a moment, cleaning its bill back and forth across the limb at its feet.

A small field mouse chose an inopportune moment to skitter forth. A moment after it had scrambled onto a dead cedar log, the butcherbird darted down to kill it.

This time the shrike grasped the lighter prey in its bill and flew to its nest tree, the locust across the creek. Flying close to the surface until a few feet from the tree, the shrike then swooped upward into the branches. There it impaled the mouse on a thorn. By alternately pulling at the head and tail of the animal, the shrike worked it firmly onto the natural hook.

Blue could see that the dead mouse had company. The shrike had hung dozens of insects and sparrows on its home tree. There were no squabs there. Squabs were too heavy. The shrike could eat the choice parts from a squab without going to the trouble of hanging it up.

Before long the bird began to sing. It was far different from the clear calls of the spring songbirds. The shrike's musical efforts consisted of rusty whistles and pipings and choked gurgles, as if somehow its voracious appetite interfered with its ability to make music. But the song was evidently natural, for the shrike twitted up and down a twig, seemingly quite pleased.

The sun was now well below the mountains. The fading sound of pig squeals indicated that there was no longer danger from that source, but the approach of twilight signaled that nocturnal animals of prey were just now beginning their stalks. The normal pattern of hunters and the hunted in the nighttime bottom land did not include the passengers. They were creatures of the open sunlit sky.

Blue watched a spider on a nearby huckleberry bush. The insect was busily rolling up its web to prevent destruction by the threatening spring storm. The horned owl hooted again. Down on the creek mud turtles slipped into the water from their perches on logs and rocks. The depths of the creek provided security from pelting rain and thunderous vibrations.

An eastern wood frog drifted with hind legs outstretched along the quiet water at the edge of the creek bank, aware of the storm but not frightened by it. The frog's throat and chest ballooned, and several explosive *clucks* reverberated as the contracting chest muscles forced air into the frog's vocal sacs. Suddenly the *clucks* stopped short. Though Blue could not see the weasel which chopped off the sound with one snap of needle teeth, he sensed that the frog had died.

After a moment Blue saw the weasel in the gathering dusk. The slender-bodied animal darted from one spot to the other, his keen pointed nose sifting the smells of each possible hiding place for prey. Pieces of bark, rock crevices, and tiny holes in the ground all received the weasel's curious nose. Twice the animal thrust its nose into the deep imprint of a pig's hoof.

An older squab which Blue had noticed a short time earlier had failed to choose a proper roost. The weasel sprang the four feet to the top of the wild plum bush and snatched the young pigeon. The bird died before it reached the ground. The weasel's flicking tongue spent a moment licking blood from the squab's neck; then its interest in the prey dissolved.

The animal seemed to be aware of other prey in the vicinity. Blue watched with tensing muscles, still awkward from immaturity, as the weasel stood with its front feet on a rock and its nose high, searching the night air for a telltale scent. The lightning to the west flashed, spilling light through the bottom lands.

Then the weasel's nose found the ribbon of air which carried Blue's scent. The animal turned and ran to the clump of sedge which sheltered the bird. Instinctive reaction at finding danger so close caused Blue to lose his balance, and he fell forward out of the broom sedge, landing a few inches from the weasel's snarling mouth.

The great horned owl had watched the weasel intently for several moments, waiting for the proper instant to sweep from the treetop, when the animal would have its full attention fixed on prospective prey.

The weasel crouched to throw itself forward and snap the squab's fragile skull. It did not see the owl.

There were only the quick shadow, the silent wings, the sudden whisper of air as the wings braked the bird; then the sharp talons gripped the weasel. The animal's shoulders and vital organs became a useless pulp at the instant that the weasel's head began to turn toward its attacker. The owl's curved beak, sharp as a thorn, nailed a hole through the animal's skull.

Blue scrambled back into the sage stalks as the owl heavily beat its way toward the hollow tree at the head of the creek.

Chapter Three

A DUCK HAWK STOOPS ON THE PASSENGERS

HIGH TIDE

THE SNOW melted by midmorning. Blue now had a yearning for food, and he joined other squabs who were busily searching for acorns and beechnuts among the leaves which were white-speckled with broken bits of eggshell from thousands of plundered passenger nests.

The older squabs found invisible foodstuffs among the leaves. Blue tried to imitate them, diligently scratching the thin springy beech leaves aside until he found a nut. He gulped it, unaware of the rich chestnut-like nut meat inside the shell. He was also unaware of the action which would take place inside his crop as the sharp stones and grit he ate ground the shell away from the meat so that his stomach could digest it.

Instinct told the young pigeon to eat the tasteless nut, the same instinct which guided Blue's kind throughout their hazardous lives, protecting them as much as they could be protected. Instinct urged him until his crop was full, and then impelled him to peck up the sharp-edged bits of flint and quartz in the loam which had been split from larger stones by roots and the freezing water of winter rains.

Hogs still roamed the nesting area, pouncing on helpless squabs caught in the open. Blue hugged the edges of the blackberry thickets so that he could jump to refuge when one of the huge bristly beasts came snorting through the underbrush.

For every security there was a danger. The blackberry thickets contained the copperhead snakes, bronzed poisonous vipers with triangular heads, who were fearful of the hogs' pointed hoofs. Blue had never seen a copperhead until one suddenly materialized from a handful of leaves.

An instant before the leaves were motionless; then they rustled in warning as the sinuous reptile probed toward Blue, an ugly creature whose body imitated the subtle browns of the dead leaves.

The snake, a young one from last spring's hatching, grazed Blue's left wing with a fang. Then it recoiled deep into the leaves. Only the tiniest droplet of poison entered Blue's body.

But for every danger there was a security. The fat which had been built into Blue's body by the forced feeding before he left the nest provided a block to the poison, allowing only a fraction of venom to filter through to the bloodstream where it could do damage.

Blue's wing hung stiff and sore for three days while the effects of the snake bite wore off.

As the older squabs around Blue hopped over and past him to get at untouched feeding grounds, Blue flapped his wings in an attempt to aid his legs in struggling past the others.

The feathers grew quickly now, the hairs being replaced by gray half-feathers which itched at their roots until Blue's bill scratched each feather follicle. This massaging spurred the feather growth, and Blue soon found himself fluttering a foot or so off the ground for short distances.

The spotted covert feathers, the short ones which clothed the wing muscles and helped to camouflage Blue against the mottled leaf layer, were now interspersed with growing flight feathers, the long stiff feathers to the rear of each wing. The primary flights grew longest, and extended each wing far beyond the limit of bones and muscle. The secondary flights were shorter, and filled out that portion of the wing nearest the body.

Each day Blue could feel the strange power growing in his wings, a power to which he gave no thought because it was not nature's intent that Blue's kind should have need to wonder about things, but only an awareness of what they should or should not do.

The muscles which lifted the wings were relatively small. Because the wing slanted down from front to rear as it lifted, and the air slipped through the top of relaxed feathers on the upbeat, these muscles did not have much work to do. The muscles which pulled the wing quickly down after each upbeat were the ones that grew stronger, developing as much as four times larger than the upbeat muscles.

As the wing came down it flared level, and the cupped feathers formed a mass which packed a cushion of air beneath them. As Blue flew, the action was much the same as that of climbing an invisible stairway into the air.

One afternoon, when Blue pitched forward into a

wooded ravine full of pin oak, a sudden gust of wind
under his widespread wings lifted him like a kite and
tossed him a hundred feet high. He beat the air frantically for a moment, trying to counter the sudden force
which dropped the ground beneath him. It was of no use.
He locked his wings wide and sailed with the wind, like
a dry beech leaf in a winter storm.

When the gust spent itself, Blue glided easily toward
a white sycamore thrusting up from among the trees on
the bank of the creek. There his pointed tail flared wide
and pointed down to act as an air brake which stopped
him an inch above the topmost limb.

He grasped it, all four toes of each foot tightly grip-
ping the limb like strangling tendrils of a rough red vine.

Blue sat there for ten minutes, neck stiff and high in
the air, red eyes alert and reflecting some of the fright
which his new experience had given him.

It required another ten minutes for his wings to stop
their nervous balancing each time the breeze whispered
at his belly feathers. When his nervousness had gone, so
had the memory of his new experience. Only an awareness that his wings would take him to better feeding
grounds remained.

Blue left the high treetop, and sailed down to the creek
bank to search the mud for salt. As his bill test-probed
the muddy silt at the edge of the clear water, his attention
was drawn to a disturbance of the surface of the creek
a few yards upstream near a shelf of rocks.

After a while he discovered the cause of the ripples.
Trout were tailing May-fly nymphs. The newly hatched
nymphs were beginning a new phase of their short life

cycle. They floated along near the bottom of the creek where the water was only a foot deep. The trout literally stood on their heads, balancing with their tails, which waved slowly against the surface above them. In this position their open mouths scooped up the insects.

Farther upstream other trout grubbed caddis larvae off subsurface rocks by lazily swimming along and biting the larvae off their perches.

Downstream Blue saw the dorsal fins of other trout bulge up from beneath the surface. The fish were eating the dark-colored nymphs as they floated to the surface. As the insects rose from the bottom, the thorax, or chest section, of each split upon reaching the surface, and the dun, or winged fly, emerged to fly away.

Curiosity suggested that here might be another excellent source of food. Blue fluttered out to a bar of rounded pebbles and waded into an inch of water to share the easily procured food.

The newborn flies were delicacies, and Blue caught them by the dozens as they broke surface, an instant before they had the power to fly away to freedom. Although he soon had eaten hundreds, his appetite seemed to make no inroad on the numbers of May flies which rose uncaught to fly away.

As Blue fed, though he was within hearing of the noise of pigs catching squabs on the ridge side, and the occasional shout of a man clubbing the young birds, he paid no attention to them. The similarity between the feeding taking place at the creek and that among the trees on the ridge had no meaning for him.

For every abundance nature had provided restraints.

One morning as Blue and a group of squabs scratched under a lone oak, a flash of gray fur darted from behind a limestone boulder. It was a fox. The animal's snapping jaws smashed the heads of half a dozen squabs before the young birds scattered.

Blue found himself in climbing flight before the animal could reach him. He beat his way up among the bright green tips of the trees, winding higher in a tight spiral until the trees below seemed tiny bushes. Other older squabs joined him, and the young flock wheeled in an ever changing formation, led by mature passengers. When the flight had grown to several hundred birds, it lifted over the ridge to fly toward the mountainside across the river.

There was no uncertainty in Blue's wings now. They beat the air easily behind. When a wind pushed at his tail feathers, he spread them wider. The stream of air swept up the side of a ridge to break in turbulence past the crest. Blue allowed the gusts to sail him along, enjoying the cool thrust of the wind which pushed him with no effort on his part.

He tested the rudder-like effects of his tail. By bending the feathers at the edge and twisting the tip feathers of one wing, he threw himself down to one side in tight banks. Once the exhilaration of this new technique so possessed him that he banked from side to side, settling like a swinging autumn maple leaf until the flock moved a hundred yards ahead. He caught up with it by the time the leaders arrived at the mountainside and wheeled the flock down in a search for danger before landing.

As more days passed, and as Blue's wings grew stronger,

he ranged farther from the roosting area each day. The mottled brown feathers which had hidden him against a leaf layer began a gradual change which would eventually give his breast the bronze of the brittle oak leaves of autumn, and his back and head the hue of scudding storm clouds.

His eyes now reflected the brightness of the reddest sumac leaves of fall. They grew keen. His steel-blue bill had become as hard as the thorns ringing the honey locust trunks on the hillsides. His wings spanned a full twenty-five inches.

The flock grew imperceptibly. Each day new hundreds joined to swell the roosts. After a month the flock was so large that the addition of a hundred thousand birds more or less would not be noticed.

The flying passenger formation resembled a gray river in the sky, the wingbeats like a million ripples across its surface. The head of the river spread out like a mountain stream during a flash flood so that the flock's scouts could check every forest for miles for food.

For some uncanny reason the passengers passed over depleted forests at an altitude of thousands of feet. The passengers knew that these areas held no nuts, and none of the birds left the flock to explore the trees.

Whenever a forest held stores of nuts the scouting pigeons led the river in a great curve to earth. The huge flock of birds made the sound of a gigantic roaring waterfall as they descended to glean the millions of bushels required to feed them each day. The nut-eating animals unfortunate enough to live in an area cleaned by the passengers either starved or turned cannibal.

When the forest had been cleaned of mast, the river of birds came into being again and flowed upward. From time to time smaller flocks joined the main stream as woodland creeks empty into a river.

A strange thing happened when a duck hawk or Cooper's hawk plunged into the flock for prey. The area of birds in the vicinity of the stoop, or attack, dived toward the ground to fly for a moment before regaining the altitude of the head of the flock. Those passengers following repeated the manuever at precisely the same spot, so that the flock resembled a river flowing down a mountain into a valley and up the other side.

There were no spotted feather coats in the flock now. All the birds were mature, led by scarred oldsters who had flown with this flock for more than a quarter of a century. Those passengers who managed to avoid the countless dangers ready to reduce the passenger population won the generous span of life allotted their kind.

The flock gradually worked its way north, keeping pace with the breath of spring on the landscape below. By early summer they settled into the vast nesting grounds in northern Michigan, near a little town called Petoskey.

The market hunters destroyed so many nests there that the flock followed the path of the honkers, the Canadian wild geese whose V-shaped formations had bored north a month earlier to Hudson Bay and the prairie provinces.

The passengers built a nesting site in the low scrub near one honker nesting area. The honkers were faithful parents, like the passengers, both parents alternating on the down-lined nests, with the gander always on guard during their thirty-day incubation period.

The Canadian northlands, although rich with food, were strange. Not the least of the phenomena disturbing to the passengers were the displays of northern lights at night. The first night that Blue saw the aurora he was alert, and waited tensely on the roosting limb for some powerful thing to happen. The next time brought no nervousness. He merely sat and watched the displays. Streamers of pink and yellow and green suddenly appeared on the horizon and marched skyward in undulating bands like writhing ghost dancers. Then the lights froze to spread rays upward and outward like a rising sun. Although the auroras appeared to rest on the horizon, they began sixty miles up, where the earth's atmosphere thinned to nothingness, and shifted upward for several hundred miles. They were formed by the radiation of the sun, which had set hours earlier.

After the nesting was completed, and when young squabs covered the ground, another one of nature's checks on the size of the passenger flock occurred.

It happened one night. The air began to breathe with a strength the birds had never experienced before. Angry gusts preceded the rising temper of a summer storm, tearing the pigeons from their roosts, and scattering them like helpless bits of paper.

The distant rumbling moved nearer with the oncoming great black thunderheads, and rose in volume whenever lightning yellowed the sky.

Rain smashed like a flapping sheet into the trees with such force as to transform feather coats into sodden coverings which weighted the passengers when they struggled into the air.

Then came sleet, beating the thin spring bark off the limbs, and knocking pigeons senseless. Crashing limbs told of overcrowded roosts, and the chatter of birds falling with them sounded above the noise of the storm.

Thousands of squabs caught in depressions on the ground gave brief squawks or died silently when the rainwater swept over them.

The storm died several hours before dawn. The forest grew silent except for the sound of an occasional bird dropping from exhaustion to splash into one of the thousands of new pools under the trees.

The sun rose slowly, slipping thin streaks of red through the layers of stratus clouds to the east. Morning revealed a naked forest, and buzzards began circling the grove where the passengers lay dead. Two bald eagles joined them. The survivors huddled miserably together until the sun could dry their wings.

Those passengers left were reluctant to leave the dead birds strewn by the thousands on the ground. The sexton beetles, scavengers of the insect world, began to burrow up into the rotting birds, and the land for five miles around reeked before the survivors began drifting south again.

As the flock once more moved through the Michigan woodlands other passengers attached themselves, and twice the flock became a part of a larger flock. Many rivers and mountain ranges were touched by the shadows of the flying birds, and several times a forest received them twice.

Two things determined the direction in which the flock moved: availability of food and absence of the market hunters. The birds always used the same roosting area each night if they were within fifty miles of it. Only when increasing numbers of hunters began to infest the roosting site would they quit it for another.

The immensity of the flock caused whole forests to be picked clean of acorns and beechnuts and various seeds, such as the red sumac clusters. So effective was the gleaning of the pigeons that the underbush received a sharp setback, for there were no seeds to furnish next year's low growth.

Many small farms in the East were denuded overnight as the passengers poured out of the forests and swarmed through cornfields and orchards. Whenever this happened, clicking telegraphs brought the market hunters on the run.

Chapter Four

CAROLINA PARAKEETS AND FLYING SQUIRREL

Chapter Eight

HATTERAS STORM

Late summer found Blue's flock exploring the broad-leafed forests in northern Virginia. The passengers guarding the flock as it fed bounced from the trees with their wings drumming a warning, whenever they were disturbed, from the time the flock settled until it swarmed away an hour or so later.

Virginia was still a lean land, although the Civil War with its farm-burning and food-stealing raiders was now a decade in the past. The hill folk with pinched faces who tried to make the soil produce a living followed the flocks on their gaunt horses until the gunny sacks behind their saddles bulged with fat birds. The hickory smoke from the ridge cabins smelled of pigeon grease for days after the passing of the flock.

But the passengers were still countless.

The flock drifted south, sifting through the fertile North Carolina swamps and acquiring a fine gloss on their August feathers by abundant feeding.

Strange parrot-like birds, the Carolina parakeets, fluttered noisily through the swamps and fields. The little green birds with yellow heads were only a foot long. Nature had daubed them with bits of color—orange face, peach-colored beak, blue eyes, a brush of gray under the tail—as a reflection of their gay activity.

Many times Blue watched them flip down into a stand of cockleburrs, chattering and scolding, like children piling off a picnic wagon, to jump up and down the cockleburr stalks, jostling one another to get the best positions.

The parakeets loved the apples ripening in the Carolina farm orchards, and a few hundred cleaned a tree in minutes.

Curiosity and a desire to remain with their kind meant the end of a flock whenever a few were killed.

Once as Blue fed in the brush of a fencerow, he watched a hundred or so birds settle into a grape arbor in a farmer's back yard. The farmer came outside with a small rifle. He shot one. When it fell to the ground the birds stopped feeding to cluster around their dead member. The farmer methodically shot all but one or two in the next hour.

Like the passengers, the parakeets loved the grain-fields. They were as effective in gleaning one.

One dusk as Blue's flock settled into a new swampland perch, Blue watched the parakeets come to their roosts. A hollow black gum split by lightning stood near to where Blue watched from a water oak. The parakeets announced their coming for hundreds of yards, chattering and scolding as they worked through the treetops.

They settled on the hollow gum tree and pushed and nudged until all were inside the trunk. There they hugged the rough tree wall, firmly anchoring themselves with feet and tail and allowing their beaks to settle onto their breasts as they subsided into sleep.

A man came from a farmhouse whose lighted window winked through the trees. He carried a bag and a stick. He walked straight to the hollow gum and began to kill the parakeets.

Before Blue became excited enough to fly away into the gathering darkness toward the center of the passenger roost, the split in the gum tree showed a mound of dead parakeets two feet high.

The passengers' craving for salt drew the flock toward the brackish sloughs which the tide washed inland from the Atlantic Coast. The birds spent several days wandering along the Carolina coasts behind Cape Hatteras, slaking their thirst in waters heavy with salt.

As the flock worked through the scrub oak on a sandbar one morning, the wind from the southeast suddenly changed to the opposite direction.

A huge cloud had formed inland, its flat base of black nimbus rainclouds supporting white bundles of cumulus clouds stacked to a height of twenty thousand feet. At the top a smooth white anvil-shaped cloud of ice crystals pointed in the direction the thunderstorm moved, toward the seacoast and the passengers. Along the leading edge of the thunderstorm tumbled dirty little clouds like rolling black stones.

Vertical lightning streaks splattered down from the dirty clouds. Seconds later thunder reverberated through the dark morning air, more awesome than the sound of the coastal defense guns which had stopped a Northern fleet at Fort Macon a few miles down the coast.

The passengers saw the danger too late. As they rose to beat their way back across the sound to the shelter of the tree-filled swamps, the thunderstorm gusts caught them and flung them like feathers before it.

The flock managed to maintain a semblance of formation, the birds struggling to stay together because of the instinct which had for so long told the passengers that with numbers lay protection.

But instinct was wrong. The frightened passengers beat futilely against the wind which pushed them farther from the coastline. In ten minutes Blue lost sight of the frothy surf of the beaches behind the thundercloud.

The rain forming a dark blue column under the storm caught up with the passengers. It was hard rain, like that at the Canadian nest site. In minutes the birds were struggling for their lives on soggy, ineffective wings.

The flock felt the slight rotation of the storm to the right, as all thunderstorms north of the equator turn. They turned their tails into the wind and tried to use it to work a passage to the edge of the storm.

Rain and turbulence forced thousands of the passengers into the spindrift from the waves. Once that low, they were helpless, and the waves soon caught them.

A break in the driving rain showed to one side of the flock's path. It was an area of light of a greenish hue. The color did not serve as a warning to the passengers. They had had no experience which would warn them.

The sky's greenish hue was a symptom of forming hail. The chimneys, or updrafts, within the thunderstorm carried rain above the freezing level, where it froze into hailstones. Some of the hail fell out from its own weight only to be caught by more powerful updrafts and swept again above the freezing level, where a new layer of ice was deposited on each stone. After this had happened a few times some of the hailstones grew to the size of apples, and finally fell out of the edges of the thunderstorm to splash the surf like schools of mullet breaking water.

The passengers flew into the hail, which cut broad swaths through the flock, one stone knocking down dozens of birds. The birds died in fantastic numbers. By the time they reached clear air only one-tenth of the flock was still airborne.

The land disappeared behind the horizon. No bright spots in the overcast showed to indicate where the sun might be. The lack of guiding landmarks made no difference to the passengers, however, for nature had provided the pigeons with a wonderful apparatus given to few living things. They had in their heads a structure called pectines, which guided the birds over regions they had never seen. It was a structure so diffcrent from the normal organs of animal life that it baffled human understanding, and could only be referred to vaguely as "instinct."

The pectines sensed two forces. One was the earth's magnetic force, which had a fairly uniform pull at any distance between the equator and the poles. The other was the Coriolis force, the effect of the world's rotation, which increased in power as it neared the poles. Whenever this rotational force crossed a line of magnetic force, it created a particular impression which was felt nowhere else except at one other spot where the same magnetic line intersected the same line of latitude. Because a second intersection of the lines was far beyond the range of normal passenger activity, they were seldom confused.

The pectines themselves were behind the eyes, extending inward like fans toward the brain.

Blue and the other survivors flapped on leaden wings along the invisible beam guiding them back to the coast. In a half-hour the long flat barrier beach below Cape Hatteras which the natives called Ocracoke floated into sight on the horizon. It took another hour to reach it.

Many beaten passengers never made it. Though they struggled to keep a few feet above the waves, hundreds settled into the white caps, still pumping ragged wings.

None of the older birds were with those who stayed with Blue all the way. The survivors dropped through the sea oats to hit the sand awkwardly, and skidded to a stop in the loose sand.

The exhausted birds lay for hours in the dunes, preening their feathers dry in the sun which finally pierced the overcast. The thunderstorm had melted into a gentle sea wind, robbed of its backbone of updrafts by the cooling sea, before Blue had enough strength to stand erect.

It was midafternoon before the passengers began pecking the burrs and sea oats. Behind the dunes were thick stands of scrubby oaks and yaupon, twisted into smooth hedges by onshore winds.

The flotsam of dead passengers began drifting ashore. A few hundred yards out, sand sharks fed on the birds; closer to shore swarmed the sea gulls and pelicans; and on shore, where a line of dead birds had already formed at the high-water mark, a bald eagle joined the gulls to feed.

Almost before the storm clouds faded on the eastern horizon the shore birds around Blue began their normal lives. Perhaps they were used to such storms, and knew sanctuaries among the trees behind the sand dunes.

Already the clean little black-and-white terns were busily diving into the water from twenty feet in the air, capturing unsuspecting small fish who swam too close to the surface. A larger bird, mostly black, and with an over-sized lower bill, came into view around the point of sand. The black skimmer flapped only inches above the water, with its red beak skimming the surface for the minute animal life which formed its daily menu.

The laughing gulls, industrious birds with black heads and white bodies, flew back and forth over the waters of the sound, searching for floating food which the storm had thrown up. When one found a morsel the others gleefully converged on it in an effort to take the food. Their cackling screeches could be heard a mile.

The larger herring gulls which had been feeding on the dead passengers gradually subsided into motion-less stances with breasts turned into the wind. Their brown-speckled bodies were not as handsome as those of the laughing gulls. Occasionally, when it seemed that the laughing gulls had found an especially choice bit of food, one of the herring gulls would lope along the sand into the wind with flapping wings until it gained enough speed to get into the air. Then the bird would fly into the chat-tering laughing gulls to make them scatter while it took the prize.

A small blue heron with head resting comfortably atop a cocked neck flew past two feet off the water, taking advantage of the cushion of air between its wings and the surface of the water so that it did not have to exert the effort required a few feet higher where no cushion could be built. The heron alighted down the beach where the grasses waded into the sea water; the bird soon became invisible.

The passengers remained on the coastal islands near Hatteras for a week, fattening on the scrub acorns, until they were driven away by a party of shooters.

Chapter Five

PILEATED WOODPECKERS

APPALACHIAN FLYWAY

By OCTOBER the passengers of Blue's flock, still number-ing thousands, turned their tails into the cool winds from the northwest. They moved in a southerly direction, and edged inland toward the heavy oak and beech stands in the southern Appalachians.

Although the flock moved south, it was not for the same reason which caused the water birds to do so. The pigeons merely gravitated to food. The generations of birds before Blue had remained in the Hudson Bay area long after snow covered the ground, for cold weather did not bother the passengers, whose bodies generated much higher temperatures than those of human beings.

Many times their migrations were to the West and back to the East, returning to the scattered tracts of oak and beech which had been visited last two years earlier. They never fed in the same area during consecutive years, but gave the forests time to build their inventories of nuts and seeds back to normal. For the same reason the nesting sites were not visited more often than once every two years. The pigeons acquired the name "passengers" because of their migrations in such huge flocks.

The Appalachians were rich in food, and Blue's flock

joined other passengers as it had done in the spring. In a matter of days the flock was again an immense thing. The birds found refuge from the market hunters in the steep-sided mountain valleys, and their roosts were not molested.

One morning Blue heard a lumberman across the ridge felling trees. The sounds were foreign to that rugged land, which was seldom visited by human beings. Giant oaks and hemlocks and pine lived out their lives on the steep rock-protected mountainsides. Many trees, aristocrats all, reared naked trunks above the surrounding foliage and became their own memorials when they died. Turkey buzzards and occasional eagles who used the dead trees as watchtowers streaked them white with droppings.

The lumberman's ax blows reverberated up the canyons. After an hour, as Blue fed on red-oak acorns, the sound of woodchopping suddenly began anew on a dead pine only a few yards away. Instantly the male passengers thrust alert heads into the air, ready to spring the flock from the trees.

Then Blue saw the source of the woodchopping. A huge woodpecker, a foot and a half long, and as big as a crow, slammed vicious blows into the tree to rip out huge chunks of dead wood, which then spun to the ground.

The bird, a pileate woodpecker, was startling in appearance. A crest of scarlet feathers and the white strips against black converging below his eyes drew attention to the powerful beak, and gave his head the appearance of an arrowhead. A short tail of stiff black feathers braced against the tree trunk combined with the bird's feet to form a strong tripod base which enabled the woodpecker to hammer such powerful blows into the tree.

Blue watched the strange new bird, fascinated by the way its beak nailed holes through the bark, then levered under one side of a section of bark as big as itself and flipped it off the tree. As the wood sailed downward the woodpecker quickly pecked up the worms and grubs left in exposed burrows.

In this manner the bird worked up the tree, making a spiral of bald trunk as the flaps of torn bark fell to cover the ground at the base of the pine. Whenever worm holes promised delicacies farther inside, the woodpecker split out triangular sticks from the trunk until the heart of the tree lay bare. No other bird possessed the power of a steel-spring neck to rip open a tree in such fashion. The possible exception was the ivory-billed woodpecker living farther south.

When the bird finished with the pine it flew down to a fallen white oak to work along its length. The oak's stump, splintered by the lightning flash which had downed the tree years ago, was full of grubs and beetles. The bird laid apart the rotten stump. When it was through, only the twisted grain of the gnarled roots held any sizable portion of the stump intact.

A few days later Blue watched a pair of pileate woodpeckers courting. Soon the entire passenger flock within sight stopped feeding to watch. The woodpeckers danced along the horizontal limbs at the top of a black gum, sidestepping on tiptoes like soldiers in cadence one minute, then like playful children the next, out toward the end until the twig bent almost vertical, then back toward the trunk. Suddenly, from the midst of the dance, one of the birds hurled itself up into the air to flutter its wings like a short-winged songbird. The other woodpecker followed. Instantly the first dropped to a limb again to continue the dance. A moment later the birds dived over the edge of the cliff to begin again in the top of a dead tree whose twisted limbs curved close to the cliff's brow. A bluejay began to scold at an animal in the grass there, and before long a wildcat pushed his head out through the grass near the woodpeckers. The pair of birds sailed down the canyon.

The pigeon flocks spent restless nights when last spring's young wildcats, intent on easy prey, slipped along the roosts to kill several pigeons with one swipe of a paw. There was also a hazard from occasional raccoons taking roosting birds, but these did comparatively little damage.

Blue and a few others were gliding back to a mountain roost one evening when they encountered the beginning of a new danger. At first it was only a speck in the sky above them, then a plummeting shadow. It became a hawk as it exploded into the birds in a cloud of feathers, and then flapped off with talons deep in a rusty yearling cock which had been flying at Blue's side.

Blue banked quickly and pumped down into the protecting trees.

The hawk was a forerunner of hundreds to come. The hawks on the entire Eastern seaboard used the Appalachians as their flyway during the fall and spring migrations.

Blue learned quickly that it was foolish to try to outfly

the hawks. His wings could pump him along at seventy miles an hour, but some of the hawks, especially the handsome peregrines, or duck hawks, could dive at two hundred. He learned their characteristics by watching their attacks on the flock. The true forest hawks, the red-shouldered and red-tailed, had short wings, and hunted the rodents among the trees, seldom molesting the flock. The falcons, such as the duck hawk, were birds of the open sky who attacked the flock incessantly. Their attacks were vicious. Normally the duck hawks climbed far above the pigeons, and dropped like a stone with talons extended to slice some unlucky passenger's wing muscle. Then they circled down to catch their falling prey.

The pigeon hawks and Cooper's hawks, nearly as fast as the peregrines, pumped on pointed wings in direct pursuit of fleeing pigeons, their long tails flaring to bank them in exact line of the pigeons' flight.

Although Blue kept an alert eye for these attacks he found his best safety in the vastness of the flock itself. He flew where passengers were thickest, and stayed clear of the fringes of the flock where the hawks whittled away. There were days during which Blue saw as many as five hundred attacks on the passengers, but the flock had grown so large again that the pigeons who fell prey were not missed. Blue found himself included in this number one afternoon.

He was flying in the middle of the flock, near the top, when he saw the duck hawk which was cruising a few hundred feet above, and which, contrary to the normal attack pattern, suddenly dived into the thickest part of the flock. Blue watched it come, preparing to bank quickly to one side, when the hawk struck a pigeon immediately overhead. The hawk's momentum carried it on to hit Blue with enough force to stun him, not completely, but sufficient to cause Blue to flutter earthward in an erratic flight which ended against the face of a cliff.

A farm boy, hiking with his hound pup, had watched the action. The dog got to Blue first, grasping him triumphantly in his mouth and flinging him from side to side. Blue did not have the strength to attempt to free himself.

The boy ran up then and took the bird from the dog. Finding life still in the pigeon, the boy shoved Blue into his jacket pocket, where the passenger slowly regained his senses as the boy jogged along.

A short time later Blue felt the boy's hand pulling him from the dark pocket. He was placed into a large box with a wire front. The boy added a bowl of dried field peas and a pan of water, then squatted in front to watch. But the collision had taken away Blue's appetite, and not until several hours had passed did he have an inclination to fill his crop. When he did he felt as good as he ever had. He paced the confines of the box until nightfall, when he hopped to the edge of the food bowl to roost.

The next morning Blue's attention was attracted to a pileate woodpecker hammering at a dead hickory at the back of the farmyard. The boy also saw the woodpecker. On the second try with his slingshot, he connected, and the bird dropped to the ground.

With a shout of triumph the boy ran to pick up the

bird. He took it to the kitchen door to show the handsome red-topped head to his mother. Then, whistling with happiness at his good fortune, he placed the bird carefully inside the box with his other prize, Blue, and sat outside until the woodpecker revived.

The newcomer blinked his eyes and looked around. He gave Blue one indignant stare and sat silently until the mother called her son to lunch.

Then the woodpecker went to work. He hopped to the back of the box to anchor his talons in the wood. His head drew back four inches and slammed into the wood where two boards adjoined. A splinter half the thickness of the board split off. In less than a dozen blows, the woodpecker had ripped out a hole large enough for him to squeeze through.

The back door of the farmhouse slammed. The boy had heard the noise.

He did not act fast enough. Blue followed the woodpecker's flight to the woods.

ROSEATE SPOONBILLS

OKEFENOKEE

THE NOVEMBER winds from the northwest blew cold. Although the mountains furnished an abundance of acorns and nuts, the warmer land to the south whispered to the restless passengers.

Blue's flock moved through Georgia, drifting toward the part of the Atlantic coast whose beaches were warmed by the subtropical Gulf Stream. The dry cottonfields, now brown with winter stalks, and bordered by limited patches of gum and pine, slowly gave way to rich swamplands which pushed up into the bottom lands from the creeks.

Soon Blue found nothing but swampland beneath him, a wild and fabulous sanctuary for many animals. It was Okefenokee, the land of trembling earth, separating Georgia and Florida. Whenever a fat black bear waded from the sloughs to set a heavy foot on one of the hammocks, or "houses," the ground beneath gave way a few inches. The hammocks were floating islands of vegetation in the grass-filled lakes which the natives called prairies.

The passengers settled into the trees at Okefenokee's border and worked their way slowly into it, growing sleeker daily on the abundance of acorns and pine seeds and worms of the low ridges which meandered among the prairie lakes.

One large island, Honey Island, in the center of the vast swamp, became a roosting place. The flock flew to it each night regardless of the distance.

Blue saw strange new animals and birds from time to time. There were sizable numbers of the rare ivory-billed woodpeckers and the Carolina parakeets. Occasional bellows echoed from the dark waters of a slough where an alligator eased nostrils up through widening circles of reflections and snorted his challenge. Brilliantly colored wood ducks flew in lonesome pairs through cypress draped with gray moss and plopped into the small nest holes hollowed out years ago by woodpeckers searching for grubs. The squawks from herons and egrets came to Blue's ears as strange sounds, but the noisy scolding of countless squirrels furnished a familiar background.

Blue and the other passengers fed close to these new animals many times. Instinct had a way of whispering to the passengers when a cottonmouth moccasin or young alligator was hungry. Then the birds stayed out of reach. But most of the time the passengers were unmolested. Food here grew abundantly for all. And there were no market hunters for the passengers.

After filling his crop to capacity each day, Blue would spend hours sitting on a limb idly answering the *coos* of other satisfied passengers or watching the lives of the animals around him.

He spent an hour one afternoon watching a young mink hunt. Although it was winter, the "dry" season when the brown waters of the Suwannee and St. Marys rivers receded, there was still a shallow hidden sea in much of the grass surrounding the hammocks. The water here in the grass was crystal clear, bubbling from hidden springs.

The young mink stood at the edge of a nearby hammock and watched the twitching of the grass stalks a few yards away. A fish caused the twitching. The fish was working back toward a slough, the natural waterway which drained the grass around the hammock. There was no time to lose.

The mink slid into the water to thread a silent path through the grass stalks. The fish, a big bass, moved just ahead of the mink. The fish tail sculled slowly as the bass picked at the bugs among the roots.

The mink made a warning misstep, and before it could move close enough the bass was in splashing flight, beating a path toward deeper water.

The race quickly became uneven. The mink, swimming under the surface, had to surge upward to gulp fresh air. The bass had no need for air, and put distance between itself and the animal. The water deepened into one of the narrow lily-covered inlets leading to the slough. The bass whipped its tail and disappeared into the deeper waters.

The mink slid ahead. The chase was not over. The fish, fooled by the deep pool near the inlet's head, had turned away from the slough. All was quiet under the surface of the pool. Floating lily pads cut off subsurface light.

After a moment Blue saw a commotion at the edge of the inlet where tree roots entered the water. Then the mink's head broke surface with the splashing fish in its jaws. The mink's sharp teeth had not entered a vital spot, and the fish's struggles were all the mink could cope with. The furred animal pushed awkwardly toward a floating log.

It should have found a resting place elsewhere.

The log came alive. It was a young bull alligator who made this inlet his private lair.

The alligator's tail knocked the mink out of the water, and only the animal's stiff body saved it from death when it hit the knee of a cypress. The fish flew from its grip. The momentum spun the mink around the knee and back into the water. But the knee of the cypress also caught the alligator's jaw and pushed it aside. The young mink needed no better advantage. His slender body dived beneath the alligator. In seconds the animal was out of the pool and swimming through the grass to the dry bank of the hammock.

The event made no particular impression on Blue. He had already come to know that for every hunter there is another hunter a bit bigger and more ferocious.

A few days later Blue watched a mink, perhaps the same one, basking in the afternoon sun. The animal jumped to its feet at the sound of swishing plant stalks. The sound was too loud to be made by the breeze. Then Blue saw the source. An Indian boy poled a dugout through the cypress bordering the hammock where the mink stood.

Quietly letting itself into the water, the mink paddled across the pool and drifted behind some water lilies. Curiosity demanded a longer look.

The boy pushed his dugout ashore and tied a dead fish to a limb which hung over the water. Then he dropped something into the water under it. The young mink watched.

When the boy had moved on out of sight, the animal pushed off to investigate. The dead fish seemed attractive. The mink wallowed up to it. A green fly was already laying its eggs in the flesh.

A short distance away Blue saw two black knobs crack the surface to send widening circles outward. The young mink did not notice. Instead it lolled along under the fish hanging from the bush. Caution argued with appetite.

Swimming to the fish, the mink reared to catch its oily tail and drag it down, his feet pushing against the dead leaves underwater.

The warning *click* came too late. Metal jaws snapped on one rear foot. The sudden pain was more surprise than hurt, and the animal yelped shrilly.

Ducking his head into the water, the mink bit frantically at the metal trap. Blood swirled in the water where the trap cut the skin.

The alligator grunted. The mink recognized it, and redoubled his efforts to free himself.

In another second Blue saw the alligator with half opened jaws streaming through the water toward the furry animal.

The mink avoided the first lunge and bit savagely back at his attacker. The water frothed for a moment; then the alligator got the mink's lean body between its jaws. A sidewise jerk of the reptile's head tore the mink from the trap. A gulp, and the animal disappeared. The alligator swam lazily off to find a basking spot.

Only a few specks of froth floated on the subsiding water. The balances had been tipped unnaturally for a fleeting instant. Here it was insignificant. There were half a hundred mink within a mile.

The winter months brought to Blue new associations with subtropical wildlife of Okefenokee.

Many times Blue stared at a long snake-like neck with a bird's head on top creating a V-shaped wake along a quiet pond. That would be a water turkey, or anhinga, known locally as the snakebird. As it swam along searching for a meal, its body was completely submerged and only the neck protruded. Whenever a startled garfish flicked past, the bird's head darted forward like a striking snake to catch its prey.

Because the anhinga's feather coat was far from waterproof, the bird climbed onto a bush in the sunlight after each fishing trip. There it preened its soggy feathers into fluff again.

A beautiful but strange bird provided one of the swampland's high-lights, the roseate spoonbill. The bird had the handsome pink coat of the flamingo. Its fluffy neck and head were white. The characteristic which set it apart from other birdlife was its huge spoon-shaped bill.

Blue watched the birds feed. They waded slowly through the shallow water swishing their bills from side to side, the sensitive nerves in the bill allowing the bird to scoop up thousands of tiny unseen fish and crustaceans from the algae-filled waters.

After satisfying their appetites the spoonbills congregated in the sunny shallows where each stood motionless on one leg, tucking the spare up under a wing. Occasionally one would stretch and yawn, clacking its peculiar bill together with the sound of dry boards.

Only a few spoonbills were present when Blue first came to Okefenokee. Most wintered in Cuba and the Bahamas in the West Indies; but as spring approached, sizable flocks moved up from Florida.

A bird which caused some excitement each time it hunted was the awkward-looking reddish egret. It stood in the shallow water, haughtily surveying its whereabouts from alert yellow eyes. When a minnow disturbed the surface of the shallows, the egret pitched forward after it, running and splashing on its long thin legs. Rarely, when a minnow escaped, the egret stopped to stand with the bronze feathers at its neck ruffled in anger, and twiched its head about, searching for the hiding fish.

A few miles inside Okefenokee usually meant an area remote enough to be untrod by humans. Occasionally a hunter managed to work his poleboat up a winding slough which penetrated deep into the recesses of the swamp. The abundant wildlife, unused to ways of people, paid little attention to them. Raccoons paused among the tree roots at the bank to watch a poleboat slide past. Unless there was a hound aboard, the raccoons had little reason to hide.

It was the same with the squirrels who played by the thousands in the treetops, undisturbed by hunters searching for deer or turkey. The squirrels had few enemies—an occasional hawk, a chance encounter with a wildcat or a rattler or moccasin on the ground.

The squirrels were too abundant. Although thousands

of hollow gum trees abounded and the ivory-billed wood-peckers dug holes in solid ones there were not enough dens to go around.

One morning Blue saw a large fox squirrel try to take over a den tree from three gray squirrels. The bigger squirrel had little trouble chasing the grays from a limb. It worked its way to the den in the trunk and was about to pop into it when the grays managed to gang up on it. The smaller animals jumped behind the fox squirrel as it turned to fight off an attack. The grays nipped at its flanks, tearing out tufts of fur. Finally one managed to sink its teeth into skin on the red's back. The fox squirrel had had enough. It fled, scurrying down the tree trunk to disappear into the undergrowth.

The wily old tom turkeys, who moved like shadows along the ground, never dropped their guard. Their enemies—the wildcats, the panthers, the hunters—were plentiful enough.

The turkeys served as swampland sentries for all wild-life. Whenever Blue heard the gobble of a tom and the satisfied *cluck* of a feeding hen, he knew that the area was free of intruders. When a warning *yonk* sounded, an invisible hand stilled the sounds of all wildlife for half a mile. Animal life froze into the cover of the underbrush and stayed there until the all-clear gobble sounded.

Sometimes a veteran turkey hunter drifted silently by poleboat down a slough to a turkey feeding ground and hid in the buttonwoods. With a thin slate scraped across the lip of a small cedar box, he produced an imitation turkey call so close to the real thing that Blue could detect no difference unless he watched the hunter.

It seldom fooled the older toms for long, however. Twice Blue sat on a perch near a hunter attempting to call a turkey within gunshot. Each time a tom answered the hunter's call with a brief gobble. Minutes later Blue would see the turkey drifting like a shadow through the underbrush to approach the source of the call from the opposite direction. Upon discovering the hunter, the tom would slip behind a tree and run silently away for a safe distance before taking to the air with a warning gobble that danger lurked here.

The bluejays and the squirrels provided noisy warnings of intruders. Blue watched three jays scream through the treetops above a stalking wildcat for a half-hour late one afternoon. Finally the cat gave up his hunt in frustration and bedded down in a fern stand until the jays grew tired and flew away.

The squirrels oftentimes ran through the trees above a lost hound for a mile to announce its presence with their vociferous chatter.

These were not the only forms of security for the swamp's inhabitants. The old bucks with the rough-surfaced antlers kept their own scouts ahead when moving. The scouts, smaller does and young bucks, always fed ahead of the oldsters, whose heavy-antlered heads were eagerly sought targets for a hunter's gun.

The bucks had their own set of tricks when a pack of marauding hounds picked up scent of twin-hoofed feet punched into the leaf layer. One morning as Blue fed on the live oak acorns near a wide slough, he heard the hounds coming. A moment later the cautious rattle of a running deer sounded in the leaves. Blue flew to a bush as a ten-point buck appeared and ran straight to the water's edge.

The buck plunged in to swim toward the opposite side. Fifteen yards out, the animal changed direction to swim parallel to shore. He turned back toward shore after a moment, and emerged in the thick brush thirty yards from the spot where he had entered the water.

The dogs galloped up shortly with tongues hanging from the sides of their jaws. Without pausing they followed the deer spoor into the water and swam in a beeline toward the opposite shore. They spent a futile half-hour there, ranging in ever widening circles, trying to pick up the air trail of the buck. Then began a more methodical search for the bush trail and ground trail which should be there but wasn't. The hounds finally gave it up and trotted toward the hunter's horn sounding in the distance.

The swamp furnished sufficient natural protection for all its reasonably alert inhabitants except one, the egret.

As spring approached large flocks of the snow-white egrets began arriving from a South American winter. Okefenokee provided a favorite nesting spot. When the birds had been there two days they began separating from the flock into pairs. Less time was spent in procuring food. The pairs drifted among the cypress trees until a limb for nest building was found which suited them.

They then began a period of close association much like a human honeymoon. Neither moved a few feet without the other following. The male sat for hours on an upper limb with the female perched on a limb two feet underneath. The female egret rarely moved from the attitude in which her head rested against her mate's side. When she did move it was to follow the male's example

of lifting wings and stretching its neck. Then the two
birds relaxed to let their necks curve around each other.

As they again separated, each slid its bill along the
other's tail plumes, the aigrettes, carefully preening each
plume and causing it to curl a little more than it normally
would.

The egrets were now wearing their year's best finery,
each bird as beautiful as the white lace flowers of the lilies
standing up from the green bogs.

After a week of this association they began building
nests, constructing them of a few sticks. The limited effort
spent in building nests was quite a contrast to the time
spent preening.

It was as nature had intended, for the warm breezes
which sifted through the spaces between sticks helped
keep them clean and free of parasites which would be
sheltered by a thick grass nest. Later, when the young
egrets were hatched, the bits of shell and refuse would
fall through the cracks.

As the young egrets burst from eggs they set up an
incessant ticking noise. The parent birds fed their young
continually, their white wings and long trailing feet passing back and forth against the dark swamp background
with undisturbed regularity.

To Blue as he flew above the egret rookeries it was like
flying over the blooming magnolias whose white blossoms
appeared as snowflakes against the dark green leaves.

The egrets would have remained undisturbed but for
their tail plumes, relatively useless to the egrets but worth
twice their weight in gold in the markets which supplied

the materials for women's hats. Fashion dictated an egret plume for the well dressed lady.

The demand for the plumes called for new efforts on the part of the egret hunters. They came to Okefenokee. Although there were never more than three or four at a time, they were enough. Their flat-bottomed boats slid under the cypress while the hunters blasted away with shotguns at the egrets, who refused to leave their young unprotected.

As the birds splashed into the water a hunter reached down to yank out the plumes which would have been shed naturally by the molting egrets within a few weeks. After a few days hundreds of bloated white birds spoiled the surface of the water. Buzzards by the dozens wheeled above and dropped down to feed on the helpless young in the stick nests. The alligators stuffed themselves until most crawled lazily onto floating logs to digest their meals.

Very few egrets escaped to the inner depths of Okefenokee. It was the carnage of the passenger nesting sites repeated.

The passengers left Okefenokee.

Chapter Seven

BLUE WINS A MATE

PETOSKEY: THE BEGINNING
OF THE END

As THE passengers moved north, spring breathed life into the forests, sending the sap searching up from roots to push out tender red shoots on the oaks and maples. The warming sun unfolded buds and spread the shoots into broad green leaves.

The yellow poplars were first, sticking up like neat green spires from the surrounding gray limbs of the forest. The maples followed, then wild cherry, sweet gums, and the oaks. The hickories came to life slowly, their buds breaking out reluctantly from tough shagbark.

Along the creeks skinny red buds suddenly burst into displays of magenta, and snowy female dogwoods scattered themselves over the hills to brighten the somber woodland, leaving the non-flowering dogwoods to slowly awaken like lazy husbands.

Rays of spring sun painted broad swaths of warmth over the ground to stir the grubs and worms in the loam under the leaves. It meant satisfied crops to Blue and the passengers. They scratched as many as fifty thousand worms from a single acre of woodland.

The cardinals welcomed the arrivals of the songsters

who had wintered in the tropics. The trees became busy roadways for flitting birds, each trying to outdo the other in singing chirps and trills. None could hold his own with the gray bird whose wings showed flashes of white as it popped from twig to twig—the mockingbird.

As the passengers wandered north they swung far to the west along the valley of the Mississippi River. Although most of the flock was made up of young birds, there were a number of oldsters who had nested for a decade in northern Michigan for which the flock now chose a course.

The springtime brought early mornings during which no wind stirred. A rooster's crow sounded for a mile through the quietness. The lack of breeze did not help flying. The passengers made no early-morning flights of any length unless it became necessary to avoid hunters or find food.

When the sun had been above the horizon long enough to dry the dew on the wild iris and azalea, the breezes were born. The plowed fields reflected more of the sun's rays than did the woodlands, and heated the air over them. As the warmer air rose, cooler air from the woodlands moved in to replace it. Thus the breezes came into being, and Blue could choose a favorable air current to help speed him along in almost any direction.

Overcast skies cut down flying drastically. The passengers took no chances on being caught in the sky under falling rain. Roosting began early on these days.

The muggy atmosphere spurred discontent, and many shoves and pecks were exchanged by pigeons alighting on overcrowded roost limbs. Seldom did a passenger get killed; but quite often a latecomer who was persistent about joining the string of birds on a bending limb soon found the ire of a dozen passengers aroused against him, and was lucky to escape with the loss of a few feathers.

The overcasts also had a dampening effect on the voices of the songbirds. Only a few had the enthusiasm to warble.

When the rainstorms did sweep toward a roost it meant uncomfortable hours ahead. The patter of rain on the spring broadleaves sounded the signal for cover. The birds pushed around in an effort to find a spot on a limb directly under the protecting cover of a bird roosting overhead, or tried to get the choice place next to the tree trunk on a limb away from the wind.

As Blue grew stronger and heavier, he moved closer to the front of the flock each day. By the time they reached Lake Michigan, Blue was among the leaders of the flock.

The flock had now reached a high population again. The addition of small flocks picked up along the way brought the total to several million birds.

Although large for its time, the flock could not approach those seen in the early 1800's when a flock could fill the sky for more than a day.

There was little wind as they left the Wisconsin shore of Lake Michigan. The thousands of younger birds who had never seen this inland sea followed the leaders without hesitation. Shortly afterward the wind died, and the passengers found themselves enclosed in fog. The flock wandered aimlessly for a time before climbing above it. Only those few passengers sick from disease or parasites had trouble keeping up. A few thousand fell into the water.

The flock settled wearily that afternoon into the luxuriant growth on the opposite side of the lake near a former nesting ground close to Petoskey, Michigan. Other huge flocks were already there. Others would come later.

The millions of wingtips made a sound resembling a huge windstorm. Within an hour the nudging and chattering stopped and the forest settled into quietness except for an occasional sqawk from a bird startled by a prowling animal.

The whippoorwills began their throaty whistles after dark, telling the woodland's inhabitants that the night would be clear. They would have called during the period of dusk if rain threatened to curtail their evening activities early.

A full moon eased over the black ridges to the east and spilled its light down the hollows, silhouetting the trees distinctly against the sky.

The nesting site covered more than 100,000 acres; it was forty miles long and up to ten miles wide in places.

The next day as the birds fed in the bushes the males stopped their feeding to perch in the undergrowth. Strange bell-like noises sounded from their throats, and grew in volume until the sound resembled a cyclone as the pigeons began courting their mates to be.

Blue's eyes were drawn to a young pink-breasted hen with cinnamon back who was the center of attention for several cocks. They fluttered about her, strutting on nearby limbs with ruffled body feathers and spread tails, competing with each other in long *coos* to attract her.

She ignored them, and backed off when one pushed against her.

The hen was a handsome bird, still resplendent in her best winter feather coat. The sunlight striking her neck splintered into a hundred reflections of green, purple, and blue. She was a young hen, perhaps from the same nesting site where Blue was born. The red skin of her legs and feet formed a perfect covering, unbroken by the wear showing on the older hens.

Blue spread wings to drop from his perch to the limb where she sat. Immediately the competing cocks turned on him. Their eyes were too full of the pink-breasted hen to notice his size and age.

Blue met them with quick hard thrusts of his beak which broke stiff wing feathers. One cock darted from the bush in fright. Within a minute the others followed his path through the bushes.

Blue began his courtship, repeated by the many male passengers in the vicinity. He jumped high into the air to make quick circular flights, meanwhile going through many maneuvers designed to win the attention of the hen.

At the height of his upward spiral Blue held his position in the air for a moment to rap the primary quills of his wings together above his back. The combined sound of many males rapping their quills made a peculiar noise resembling that of a hailstorm pounding deciduous trees in summer.

After a period of this, Blue settled beside the hen to gently nudge her bill. When he opened his bill and she placed hers crosswise in his the courtship was at an end.

The pink-breasted hen now belonged to Blue.

After two days Blue and his mate began their nest with a few odd twigs picked up at random. The hen directed the nest building, uttering a soft *coo* when she was ready for Blue to get another twig. When a few dozen had been clumsily stacked together, much like the egret nests, the hen settled on the nest and laid two eggs.

She warmed the eggs during the night. Blue took her place in midmorning and remained there until late afternoon, when she sat again. During the time off the nest each bird fed in the forests and grainfields fifty to one hundred miles away.

The nests were built in each tree in such unbelievable density that it seemed as if not a single limb or twig fork was left exposed. Huge stiff oaks began to droop at the limb ends in the manner of weeping willows. Many branches were so overloaded with nests that when an extra pigeon alighted, the limb splintered at the trunk and a hundred nests and their contents spilled to the ground. This overcrowding of nesting trees invited further disaster. A rain shower or wind gust brought hundreds of limbs to earth.

The passengers never learned. Those rendered nestless by a falling limb merely built another nest in the nearest overcrowded tree to see the same destruction repeated on many occasions. Passenger instinct did not allow the economical scattering of nests such as those the turtledoves built.

Near Blue's nest was the small grass nest of a sparrow in a bush a few feet off the ground. The mother sparrow had no sooner left her nest to feed one morning when a drab gray bird, a cowbird, settled into the nest. When she left it a few minutes later, she left her large speckled egg. The returning sparrow mother did not notice the addition. She settled onto the eggs with fluffed feathers to give them the warmth which would awaken the life deep inside the yolks.

All the sparrow's eggs hatched at about the same time, and the busy mother was hard put flitting back to the nest with enough bugs and worms to feed the hungry little beaks which opened upward.

At the time of hatching, the young cowbird was larger than the young sparrows. As a result it was able to out-reach the others and grab the great majority of food. Within a week it had so outgrown the others that it shoved them from the nest to starve on the ground.

The mother sparrow faithfully fed the young cowbird. In days it had outgrown the nest and perched atop it, half feathered, but still unable to fly. In another two days the young cowbird moved out onto a limb and tested its wings. The mother sparrow still fed it, although it was now larger than herself.

Blue saw the last of the two the next morning when the cowbird flapped from bush to bush until it was out of sight, with the protecting mother sparrow following, still intent on feeding it until it could fly away from her.

Blue didn't see the yellow warbler a half-mile away that returned to her nest to find a cowbird egg among her own. She spent the afternoon building an insulating layer of grass across the entire nest of eggs. Then she settled down to lay another nestful. Nor did Blue see the robin who stared suspiciously at the brown-speckled egg deposited among her light blue ones. She promptly kicked the strange egg out.

At the end of two weeks, when the eggs of Blue's hen cracked to reveal young ones, he searched more diligently for food so that there would be plenty of the curd secreted in his crop with which to feed the young birds.

He found a new feeding place one afternoon, a field of close-growing grain stalks. It was soon filled with pigeons who pecked the unusually large amount of grain scattered on the ground.

Soon after alighting, Blue halted his feeding to gaze at the man who stepped softly from the bushes. Because the grass prevented Blue from seeing, he hopped to the edge of the grain stalks.

A snap sounded, and a huge circular net rose from the adjacent grass. Blue's legs shoved hard, and he bounced into the air, beating his wings together in a danger signal.

The birds on the ground took up the noise instantly, but it was too late. The descending net met them as they rose, and knocked them back into the grass, where it held them.

Blue circled excitedly above the net while the man pulled pigeons from it, killed them, and packed them in a basket.

After the man left, Blue settled back into the field only a short distance from the catch. Somehow nature had not provided the passengers with enough instinctive suspicion.

When several hundred pigeons had joined Blue in another feeding area, there came another snap. This time Blue was quicker, but he barely escaped the wooden rim of the net. Less than a dozen passengers escaped with Blue.

Blue left the valley of nets and winged back to the nesting site. He knew something was wrong long before he reached it.

The popping sounds of several hundred shotguns rose from the trees which harbored the nests. The market hunters had arrived in force. Blue could see confused passengers milling in the sky above.

Men ran back and forth under the trees, picking up dead pigeons and shooting at those who remained alive in the trees. Men with clubs were killing the fallen squabs.

Dropping down between the tree crowns, Blue banked and stalled on cupped wings to the edge of the nest where his hen still sat. An ugly gap in the feather line at the back of her neck showed him that they could no longer use the nest.

After nudging the hen to her feet he forced her to fly, and then beat his way upward, signaling to her to follow.

As they rose and circled, others of the drastically thinned flock fell in behind Blue. He led the column of several hundred birds away to the south until a half-dozen streams had slipped beneath them; then they settled again into the treetops. Other surviving portions of the original flock were scattering in other directions. All were confused.

Blue watched the excited birds hopping in the limbs. They seemed lost; but soon they were busy on the ground, pouncing on grubs and seeds with too much energy, as if in compensation for being driven from their nests. The birds kept up their agitated cooing far into the night.

When the sun rose again Blue beat his way against a headwind back across the streams to the nesting site. He could see that the woods were still alive with hunting men.

He slipped down into a stand of pine not far from a group of the men. They were picking up dead passengers from a huge pile and cutting open the bellies of the dead birds, to spill out worm-like innards, which gave off a bloody, sickening smell.

Blue wanted to leave, but the work of the men drew him. He could not understand their actions. He watched, fascinated, as stripped passengers were thrown into pails of water and were then pulled out to be jammed shapelessly tight into wooden barrels as big as the men.

Men were rolling the barrels onto horse-drawn wagons which moved down a muddy road to the railroad or to the ports on Lake Michigan. The wagon roads had already become featherbeds paved thick with wings, feathers, and tails from the pigeon-dressing operations. Drivers intent on adding another five-dollar bill to their rolls for each trip urged sweating horses through the ruts. Every few hundred yards a muttering driver returning with an empty wagon had to pull off into the trees to allow a loaded wagon to pass.

The tent camps of farmers from miles around were pitched anywhere a level spot could be found. It was too much to expect a clean camping site. The stench of thousands of half rotted passenger carcasses permeated the entire forest, and the fly-ridden skeletons of those overlooked by the market hunters lay thick among the leaves.

Women and children in the tent camps appeared not to

notice the odor. They were too busy canning passengers or rendering the fat from squabs in black washpots. Indians from the northwoods had set up their camps to do the same thing.

Toward the middle of the nesting site sounded the constant ring of axes chopping down trees loaded with nests. Duller sounds were made by other men hitting saplings with sledgehammers to shake the squabs from their nests. Some climbed the trees to poke the squabs out of the nests with sticks.. Many of the young birds were so heavy that their bodies broke open when they hit the ground.

As the hunters scurried about each downed tree they grabbed the squabs, jerked off their heads, and threw them on the bloody pile of birds near the wagon-loading point. It made little difference here that pigeon blood splattered the bushes and made stinking little pools in the wagon ruts.

The instinct of self-preservation in the passengers was subdued by the one which said that their young must be protected. Setting passengers hovered nervously over squirming young and watched the slaughter. Very few had followed the example of Blue and his hen.

The destruction went on for months. At this one nesting site it began in March and continued until August. The only thing that could stop it would be the disappearance of the passengers or a drastic drop in the market price of the birds.

But there was little chance that the price would drop. The pigeoneers consistently sold their catch for fifty cents a dozen. In the big cities the retail price ranged up to twenty cents a bird. About five hundred professional pigeoneers worked the Petoskey nesting site, and five thousand more earned a full-time living elsewhere as market hunters. Many more thousands hunted the birds during their spare time.

Blue skirted the pine tops to wing his way back to his tiny flock. He led them now, away from the setting sun toward the mountains which he knew to be in the east.

Chapter Eight

THE BAITED MUD FLAT

STOOL PIGEON

BLUE POINTED his tiny flock toward Cygnus the swan, or Northern Cross, and Aquila the eagle, the two constellations who flew forever in their sanctuary in the Eastern summer sky.

Blue brought the flight closer to the ground each hour. The passengers' appetites for food became secondary to a craving which could not be satisfied with beech mast.

The birds craved salt. The manufacture of the curd in their crops to feed their young at the nesting had drained salt from their systems. Their bodies clamored for the substance to be replaced immediately.

As a result Blue banked the flock toward those clumps of trees in the ravines which might mean the presence of salt springs. Within a period of two hours Blue dropped the flight a dozen times to the banks of small streams, never finding water or mud with enough salinity to do more than torment and increase their craving.

An hour before dusk Blue spotted a marshland to the south of their path. He circled the flight above the marsh while he flew lower to investigate. The cattail growth was untrampled by man, and the mudbanks revealed no footprints. The place seemed safe enough.

Blue turned the flock down. The birds alighted on the largest mudbank, the only one clear of grass and stubble which might allow preying animals to creep up unseen. The passengers, like the turtledoves, always picked an open space, if available, to feed and drink.

Blue plunged his bill into the mud. It was there. The mud was as briny as a wet sea beach.

The other birds followed his example. Even the lookouts bent to slake their craving for the delicacy. The salt acted like a powerful stimulant on the digestive glands in the pigeons' bodies. Like a flash flood turned loose on parched land, for a few moments the flock dissolved into a boiling mass of crazed birds, each frantically driving its bill deep into the mud, oblivious to toes or heads which got in the way. A dozen toes were lost in half that many seconds.

The salt was strongest in the center of the flat. It drew the passengers to it until they were one compact mass of fluttering feathers.

The net caught them that way. Not one escaped, not even the lookout birds who remained at the edge of the circle.

Most of the passengers forgot the salt and struggled to escape. The pink-breasted hen pushed through the pigeon mass toward Blue, and together they struggled toward the edge of the net.

Blue spotted a tear. He was only a few inches from it when the man stepped from the cattails and yanked the drawstring along the net's edge, effectively closing the gap.

The man fashioned the net into a huge bag and dragged

it over to the cattails, where large baskets fashioned of white oak splints were stacked. The man separated them. On the bottom of the stack was a wooden cage.

The man pushed his hand into the mass of pigeons inside the net, his fingers feeling the wing muscles of the birds. The first-year squabs with softer wing muscles and thick breasts were bypassed. The older birds were not.

Two dozen were selected for the cage before the man's fingers squeezed around Blue's wings. As the man lifted Blue from the net, the bird shoved hard with his feet, far enough to free his wings.

The man's fingers grasped Blue's tail as the struggling bird flapped hard before his eyes. The pink-breasted hen, following close behind, took advantage of the confusion of the moment to burst free like a feathered rocket which straightened in flight inches above the cattails and was gone from sight in seconds.

The man cursed and flung Blue hard into the cage. Another ten cents lost.

The man stuffed another dozen passengers into the cage before he tied the door shut with string. Then he began a grisly process which Blue could not fathom. The bird could only watch in bewilderment, sensing that something was happening that was sapping life from the passengers in the net, yet unable to understand what could cause a live pigeon to be transformed in a half-second into a dead fluff of feathers from which a leg kicked a time or two before it stiffened.

The man's hand held a pair of pliers whose nippers had been spread slightly so that they did not quite meet. With these the man methodically crushed the passenger's heads like walnuts and dropped the birds into the baskets. The bent-plier method prevented blood from getting on the ground to scare away other passengers.

Nearly an hour had passed before the man emptied his net and loaded the baskets and cage onto the wagon waiting under the trees at the edge of the marsh. Blue spent the night crammed in the cage, which was dropped off at the livery stable where the man rented his rig.

At sunrise the man loosed the passengers into a chicken pen which gave them room to stretch their cramped muscles. Blue joined the others in eating the grain on the floor of the pen.

Shortly afterward the man snatched up Blue and two more birds and dropped them into a burlap bag. Blue felt the hard bouncing floor of the wagon beneath him for an hour. Then the man fished out Blue.

After blinking his eyes in the bright morning sunlight, Blue found that he had been returned to the same spot at which he had been captured.

Though Blue did not struggle as the man tied a string to his leg, when the hunter placed him on a stick thrust in the center of the salt flat the bird flung himself into the air with pumping wings. The string allowed him to fly two inches. After several seconds of upside-down struggling, Blue beat his way back up to a perch atop the stick. Again he tried to fly free, and again he failed.

The string jerked. Blue fluttered a moment before regaining his balance. The man had pulled the string from his hiding place in the cattails.

Blue was a stool pigeon now, a decoy to passing flocks.

The man picked up a bag of salt and sowed it over the mud.

Action was not long in coming. A flock of passengers appeared to the south. Blue saw the man stand up from his hiding place and toss a pigeon into the air. The bird quickly took advantage of its freedom and pumped upward.

At a hundred feet the bird stopped as if it had met an invisible wall. Its wingbeats could carry it no higher, and Blue watched it slowly lose altitude even while its wings beat hardest.

Then he saw the reason. A cord stretched from the bird's leg to the man, who slowly drew the bird downward. Blue looked off to the south. The leaders of the flock had seen the flying decoy and had already turned their passengers toward the place where a pigeon seemed to be alighting.

The man drew the flier down to his hiding place and shoved it in the bag. The moment the flock got within sight of him, Blue felt the string on his foot jerk. To keep from falling he reared his body and flapped his wings. The man continued to pull the string.

As Blue fluttered, he saw the leaders sweep over the salted marsh. They could see only the fluttering passenger, apparently in the act of alighting on a stick. The flock dropped to the mud, paying no attention to Blue's attempts to warn them.

The occurrence of the day before was repeated. The birds went crazy over the salt. The net rose and fell. The man filled a half-dozen baskets with dead birds.

The same process was repeated once or twice a day

for a week. It was on the sixth day that the pink-breasted hen found Blue.

Blue did not see her coming as he sat on his perch. She swept in over the cattails, then rocketed past him to wheel and sweep past once more. Blue flung himself from the perch, but his strongest efforts could not break the string.

The pink-breasted hen alighted in the top of an oak a half-mile away at the edge of the marsh. She was there each morning during the next few days when the market hunter brought Blue out and tied him to the perch. She spent most of each day there, except for short feeding trips and an occasional flyby for Blue's benefit.

Once, when the man sent up his flier to attract a passing flock, a peregrine falcon, dropping in a stoop which began two hundred feet above, hit it. A thud, a puff of feathers, and one wing separated from the collision, the falcon's talons slicing through shoulder muscle and bone to cut off the wing. The falcon then made a quick pass to grab its prey, but the string held by the angry market hunter prevented the falcon from flying away. The attacker soon dropped its prey. The hunter lost two more fliers in the same way that afternoon.

One day Blue found himself left in the livery-stable cage. The market hunter had other things to do. As Blue watched, he saw other market hunters engage in a cruel practice which had originated in the Middle East. They sewed the eyelids of live passengers shut as the falconers of the Asiatic countries did to their hawks in training them. The pigeons, however, were to be used for a different purpose. They would be stool pigeons as Blue had been. Several would be placed in the branches of a bush near a baited bed, and when the hunter shook the bush the birds would flutter to keep their balance, yet unable to fly away because of their blindness.

The next day Blue saw the reason for the absence of the market hunter who had caught him. The man took Blue and several others to a baited bed a mile from the salted marsh where he had built a low pen of wire, thirty feet long and open at the top. To one side was secured a net large enough to cover the pen's top when the bent saplings anchoring it were sprung.

The hunter tied Blue and several other birds to stakes in the center of the pen, then sprinkled huge amounts of beechnuts, anise seed, and salt in the pen and close around it.

Within an hour a flock dropped into the pen, lured by the feeding decoys. They soon packed it so tightly that the ground could not be seen for the crawling bodies of the pigeons.

The net snapped down. This time the hunter pushed the birds into the feeding pens built into the sides of the trap. When he had finished, he rigged the pen again for capture.

Unfortunately, the pink-breasted hen chose the moment to find Blue again. She came sailing out of the sky like a drifting autumn leaf. Unaware of danger, she dropped to the ground a few inches from Blue.

A small flock, seeing her flight, settled into the pen behind her. Blue aimed frantic warning pecks at her, but the pink-breasted hen deftly stepped aside and out of reach, enjoying the bit of play.

The net sang through the air again, closing the pen with the ease of a moving shadow.

Because of the hen's determination to stay close to her mate, the two were packed in the same shipping crate that night. After grain and water had been placed in the box, it was moved to the railway station to be stacked among a hundred others containing cooing agitated pigeons. There were no first-year squabs in these crates; all were older birds with flight-hardened muscles. The shipping tags were addressed to a dozen different shooting clubs scattered over the Northeast.

Blue spent the next three days on a clattering train headed east. An overcast hid the sun, and rain drenched the pigeons huddled miserably in the drafty dampness of the crates. Many, unable to change from the clean life and food of the outdoors to the dirty food and water of the crates, died.

Blue and his hen looked out through ruffled feathers and sore eyes on the fourth morning to see several of the crates being unloaded onto a station platform. The box containing Blue was among them.

Later in the morning a wagon hauled the crates into the country to a shooting club where they were emptied into a huge wire pigeon loft. Clean food and water did much to lift Blue's spirits.

Two days later the grounds of the club began to fill with men carrying guns. Most wore city clothes. There were none of the rough outdoor clothes of the market hunters.

Men came into the pigeon loft and herded the passengers back into crates. Blue's hen remained close to his side and followed him into one of the crates. Someone picked up the box containing Blue and carried it out to the shooting grounds.

Already the blasts of shotguns sounded steadily, coming from little groups of people standing on various rises of ground. Blue soon saw what it was all about. A live-pigeon shoot had attracted the club members.

An attendant in concealment tossed one of the speedy targets into the air. The passenger, confused momentarily before straightening in escape flight, usually crumpled in mid-air before a blast of shotgun pellets. Those passengers that did not hesitate but flew low and fast escaped the gantlet. Most failed to do so.

A half-hour passed before an attendant's hand grasped Blue's body. The man tossed him a dozen feet into the air. Blue came right back down with pumping wings that hurtled his body at sixty miles an hour three feet above the grass. He cut down a twisting shallow gully between the groups of shooters toward the mountains and trees to the north.

A half-dozen blasts sang past Blue. He was well past the last shooters when a last gun sounded. Two of the tiny pellets made contact, one searing feathers off a line at his back, the other cutting out a primary flight feather near the end of a wing.

Except for the disturbance of his equilibrum in flight, no damage was done, and Blue sailed into the nearest trees at the foot of a ridge a half-mile away.

Two more birds from his crate fell before the shotguns before Blue's hen came out. She attempted to follow Blue's example, but a gust of air tossed her even higher than the attendant's throw and she lost a precious second in coming back down. The shotguns were aimed more accurately at her than they had been at Blue.

The last group of marksmen blasted her as she shot past. She dropped into the grass a hundred feet farther on.

Blue saw the whole incident. Hugging the contours of the ground, he flew back to the spot where she fell, and dropped beside her. She was not dead. Her eyes were open. A freak hit had grazed her head and stunned her.

At Blue's urging she stood. After another moment she was ready to fly. With Blue in the lead the pair bounded into the air just as a retriever romped up.

Blue took his hen high on the mountainside to a huge white oak with heavy foliage. There the two passengers settled on a limb and rested for an hour, knowing once more the feel of the free sky.

Chapter Nine

LAST OF THE LABRADORS

THE CATSKILLS

A month was required for Blue and his hen to find enough scattered passengers to make up a flock of about two hundred. He took them to the Catskill Mountains. The carnage at Petoskey would not be erased from their remembrance for a long time. Blue intended to find a sanctuary which would last until a nesting had been completed.

They searched the valleys and hillsides, following the contours of the mountains, never soaring more than five hundred feet above the ground in order to scout the area thoroughly.

They searched the Northeast for several days, ranging as far north as Mount Katahdin, which reared nearly a mile high from the Maine wilderness. Katahdin lay like a giant fishhook. At the point of the hook a huge rounded dome, Pamola, named by the Indians for a god they feared, looked down on three basins from granite cliffs hundreds of feet high.

Though Pamola indicated sanctuary to the passengers, Blue did not like the area. The woodlands were mostly coniferous, and he wanted ground covered with beech mast to feed the squabs until they would be ready for flight.

To the south a few days later Blue found a place to his liking, a hillside of beech leeward from the prevailing wind. There were no white lines of trails or roads in the vicinity, and he knew that the hunters could not reach them easily. Only an occasional hawk circled. It seemed an ideal place.

The beeches were huge and sturdy. The thick layer of leaves on the ground formed a protecting cover for last autumn's beechnuts, three-sided and thin-shelled, whose rich sweet nut meats would spur the growth of the squabs when the time came for them to shift for themselves.

The beech forest was unique in that it still existed. It reflected the magnificence of the stands of beech of a half-century ago, when great tracts of woodlands were formed of thousands of these huge but graceful trees whose smooth blue-gray bark mirrored the serenity of the undisturbed wild.

Unfortunately, the beeches liked best to send their roots into the rich loam above limestone. The farmers like that soil best also. Because for generations the beeches had revealed to the frontiersman the place to build his cabin and clear land, miles of beech forests shrank before creeping grainfields.

Already from the Ohio north the beeches had become lonely refugees existing on the fringes of cleared land— the ravines and creek bottoms where it was not worth the trouble to clear the soil for crops.

It was unfortunate for the passengers, too, for the beech tree in abundance was one of the principal producers of food in quantities sufficient to sustain the fantastic passenger flocks which had roamed North America during the centuries before the coming of colonists. The passengers once had been the most numerous of American birds.

Blue and his hen seemed to sense an urgency. They threw their nest together hastily, and two eggs were laid. Both Blue and his hen took especial care to warm the eggs. When time came for one to leave the nest to feed, the other fluttered up behind with bill touching the tail of the departing bird.

The passengers never flew singly to the feeding grounds. All the males alternated at the same time with their mates, and flew as a flock to feed. They returned as a flock and took over the nests at the same moment. The hens also flew as a flock.

The feeders ranged from the nesting site for a hundred miles in all directions. They selected their food with greater care as hatching time approached.

One afternoon Blue and the other males wandered to the New England coast. As he fed in the low growth, Blue saw a man poling a boat along the edges of the rushes growing in the quiet water on the leeward side of an island. The boat held a half-dozen dead Labrador ducks, black-and-white birds which Blue had seen a few times along the coast.

Feeding Labradors paid little attention to the boat or to the blasts of the man's shotgun. He was able to move directly into a group of swimmers and begin shooting before the ducks would take wing and fly a short distance away.

The ducks never reached restaurant tables, for they tasted fishy. But their feathers made excellent stuffing for pillows, and they were easy to kill.

The boatman poled to shore not far from a scientist from one of the state universities. The scientist stopped his work of collecting shell animals from among the reeds and strolled over to the boat.

"Hello."

The man in the boat returned his greeting.

"Quite a haul you have there."

"Fair. Couple years ago I could have filled this boat in an hour. Now I couldn't do it in a year."

"Looks like the Labrador ducks are getting killed out," the scientist suggested. "Somebody's going to have to slow down on their shooting one of these days."

The boatman looked up indignantly. "What do you mean? You trying to tell me, backhanded-like, that I better stop shooting my own ducks?"

The scientist smiled. "Yours?"

"Sure. I've always lived on the coast here. I hunt the ducks on my own property. Ducks on my property belong to me."

"They stay on your property all year?"

"Nope."

"Do you know where they nest and spend the rest of the year?"

"Nope. Don't give a hoot. Probably around here somewheres."

"Well, I'll tell you," the scientist said. "They breed a thousand miles north of here. They spend most of each year up the coast. Any particular duck probably spends only a week or so in any one place. Other folks figure the same way—kill anything on their property regardless of who feeds it."

The scientist shrugged. "It's too late now anyway. There is no protection for them. You won't see any Labrador ducks next year."

The boatman swore under his breath at the intruder. He poled his boat toward three ducks swimming into the reeds a hundred yards away.

They were his last take. There were no more Labrador ducks.

Foxes roamed the mountains in large numbers, and Blue remained alert when he fed on the ground. Twice while Blue watched, a crouching fox captured a fat passenger as the male contingent fed.

They found themselves in greatest danger when they fed at dusk, as they did on occasion when the hens returned late in the afternoon to take over the egg warming.

A half-dozen males were caught by the foxes early one evening. The foxes tolled the passengers in the same manner they did ducks.

During one night of early moonlight, Blue saw the method from the beginning. A pond lay to one side of the area in which the passengers fed. The rising moon on the far side of the pond silhouetted a group of ducks on the water.

A movement at the pond's edge drew Blue's attention. The movement was a regular one, back and forth, and repeated.

It took a long time for Blue to distinguish what made

the movement. It was a fox, steadily loping in a circle. As Blue watched, the circle grew steadily smaller. Blue's attention shifted to the ducks. They were much closer to the shore now, all intent on the actions of the fox. Their curiosity would not allow them to ignore the strange exhibition.

The fox drew his circle tighter, its center only a few feet from the water's edge. Soon the circle was finished. The fox reared high on his hind legs. He danced. After a moment he bellied down against the sand.

The hypnotized ducks waddled slowly ashore. They closed on the spot where the movement had stopped.

The woodland seemed quiet for a moment. Night sounds made no impression on Blue's hearing. He could see the crouching fox only a few feet away from the ducks. A startled squawk sounded.

The forest grew quiet again except for the fading wing-beats of the ducks.

The pigeons reacted like the ducks when a fox chose to toll feeding passengers. The animals took another dozen pigeons during the next few nights before the lack of adequate moonlight put a halt to their tolling.

Daily flights for food began to grow dangerous, especially when the passengers drifted near grainfields. One or two were killed each day by occasional gunners, and though the hunters cut down the size of the meager flock they had little effect on the nesting. Single parents restricted their hunt for food to the noonday periods when the sun provided a poor substitute for the body heat of a setting bird.

One morning Blue saw a man wandering through the

beech near the nesting site. The man's binoculars had no meaning for the passenger.

The next afternoon a boy with a rifle wandered into the nesting site and shot two passengers. As he picked them up and started back down the hill, he met the man Blue had seen the morning before. This time the man had several companions, men and women.

The man stopped at the sight of the boy and stared at the passengers in surprise. "You killed these?"

The boy stared back. "Sure, just now."

One of the women interrupted, "And what do you propose to do with them, young man?"

The boy smiled. "Eat them for supper. What else is there to do with game? Pigeons are better than chicken."

The woman looked at the boy sternly. "Aren't you ashamed of yourself?"

"Why should I be?" the boy asked.

"Don't you know that passenger pigeons will soon be extinct? We haven't seen any except these in five years. It's such a pity to see people killing them."

The boy countered. "Well, there's no law against shooting pigeons for game, I reckon." He shrugged his shoulders and moved on down the hillside toward his home.

The man and his companions trudged to the center of the nesting site. There they climbed into the trees which held the greatest number of passenger nests.

Taking small bags from their pockets, they pushed the birds off their nests and filled the sacks with passenger eggs. Then they let the bags down to the ground by strings.

Back on the ground, they counted their haul.

"How many do you have, Elbert?"

"Sixteen."

"Fine. We've got forty-six in all. This will give us plenty for our collections. Perhaps we can even give away a few at the next meeting of the Society."

One of the women was beside herself in satisfaction over the find. "And to think we had thought passengers were gone from this area for good!" She paused to fondle two of the eggs in her hand. "Doesn't it make you want to cry? I have no doubt that this is the last flock of any size we'll ever see in this part of the country."

The other woman looked at the bewildered passengers as they hopped from limb to limb in a fruitless search for stolen eggs.

The woman said: "Poor helpless creatures. Hunters are so greedy!" She clucked her tongue in pity as she remembered. "That horrible boy!"

Chapter Ten

GHOST WINGS

GHOST WINGS

THE REMAINING eggs were nearly ready to hatch when the forest fire came. At first there was only the rich sweet smell of distant smoke much like that of the river boats on the Ohio. Then, as the line of crackling flame writhed closer through the underbush, the smoke became acrid and choking.

Blue remained as long as he could, then flushed the hen from the nest and led her up through the hot smoke. Some of the other passengers waited a little too long.

After four hours the smoke had cleared, and Blue and his hen flew back to the nest. It was gone like the others at the site, burned completely. There were no other pigeons around. Blue could not understand their disappearance.

They spent the next days searching for their kind. Days became months, and years. They found none. They made aimless flights that probed into the cold winds creeping down from the north. The roosting places of Blue's youth held no passengers.

The pair made a number of nests and hatched most of the eggs; but something always happened to the squabs, either in the nest or on the ground.

Once Blue and his hen joined a dozen turtledoves as they stalked along a field of harvested peas, gleaning the leftovers. Even before Blue spread wings to sail down to join them, he knew they were not passengers.

The doves were small and thin, like undersized passengers. They took flight when Blue alighted, their wings beating the air to make a soft winnowing sound like that of whirling rope.

Puzzled, Blue and his hen waited a moment before following them. When the doves settled at the far edge of the field and Blue glided down near them, they did not take flight again, but allowed the passengers to join them in their feeding.

The turtledoves were as handsome as Blue's kind. A rich tan, the color of the sides of a young whitetail doe, covered most of the birds' bodies. Here and there bits of pink, yellow, and dark brown showed.

The doves made little noise as they fed. Only once did a characteristic soft *coo* sound from one of the pairs.

When a boy climbed over the rail fence into the field, the doves jumped into the air and flew to the bottom land along a creek a half-mile away. There they settled into a sour gum tree and continued their feeding on the blue berries remaining on the twigs. Satisfying their appetite for the berries, the doves dropped to an old road which forded the creek. There they pecked the small gravel from among the stones in order to fill their crops with the grinding material necessary to digest their food.

Nature had given the turtledoves a protecting instinct which the passengers did not share. The smaller doves did not depend on numberless flocks for survival, but on caution. Mating doves scattered their nests through acres of trees, and the small groups of birds which fed and roosted together did not draw predators and hunters as the huge passenger flocks had done.

Blue and his hen left the turtledoves the next day. A week later they joined a flock of homing pigeons who lived among the farms near a small town. At night, when the homing pigeons chose barn lofts for roosts, the two passengers found trees with thin foliage at the edge of open fields so that no intruder could approach. The day-time mingling with the homers caused a horde of lice to seek the clean feathers of the passengers. It took days of dust baths in the fields to rid themselves of the parasites. They left the homing pigeons.

As the wings of the pair grew stiffer with age, they wandered southward and along the wildernesses of the Mississippi. Blue had no comprehension of the disappearance of the once numberless flocks. There had been millions of passengers—now there was only his hen. There was no way to bridge the gap, to understand why his kind had vanished. There were only the pectines behind his eyes to guide his flight when a morning river boat caused him to remember the Ohio side-wheelers which churned by the nest where he had begun his life.

And because instinct told him that he and the pink-feathered hen must build a nest again before it was too late, and begin again their kind, they glided one afternoon into the bottom-land forest along the Ohio.

The nest was placed carefully in the fork of an oak, high above the ground. The hen laid two eggs, and Blue moved quickly onto them whenever the hen had to forage.

When the hen relieved him on the nest, Blue would flutter impatiently skyward to search the far distances for passengers. Many times the wind playing in the crowns of the tree whispered in imitation of the sound of distant passengers, but the ghost wings never materialized. Blue often followed tiny specks, only to find after each exhausting chase that they were homers or doves. The flights were gone.

Food became scarce in the forest because of an over-population of squirrels and rats and other birds, and Blue had to search carefully for foodstuffs.

The eggs had a week to go when the frost came. Blue was on the nest that morning.

A faraway gun explosion sounded soon after sunup, making him tense for long moments. The sound of other guns came through the crisp air, and Blue saw a hunter cross a cornfield with several squirrels jogging at his belt.

Blue followed the sounds of the approaching hunter as the man came closer. He glanced frantically along the treetop skyline, searching for the hen. She still had not come when the crunch of leaves below told of the man's nearness. Finally Blue picked up the hen's casual path over the trees while she was still a dot. He started once to roar away to intercept and warn her, but he knew that the penetrating cold would steal quickly into the un-hatched eggs to kill the hearts that were just beginning to beat. As the hen drew closer he caught himself again, about to flutter up; but he realized that his flight would give the location of the nest away. He settled back with rigid body.

The hen sailed over the crown leaves of the nearby poplars and floated lazily on the cushion of air under her wings. She settled into a straight glide to the nest.

Blue watched the hunter. The man had not seen. The hen was still coming; neither had she. As she rocked in easy flight, her wings rustled crisply in the cold air.

The hunter turned. Blue shrilled a warning, and the hen stalled in surprise. An explosion shattered the quiet, and the pink-feathered hen dropped.

Blue shrank over the eggs, knowing that he could not move if he would live. He became a knot on the oak limb until the man picked up the dead passenger and wandered on out of sight.

Long after the forest had regained its peace and there was no danger, Blue hugged the eggs. Instinct told him to protect them, but hunger wrestled with his instinct. He must leave the nest for food if he would remain alive to warm them—but if he left for only a short time the chilling cold would kill them.

Blue stretched a too short neck over the edge of the nest to peck at the tree bark, tearing and digging under it, trying to find non-existent bugs.

He shredded the inner bark; and though he rebelled at its bitterness, he gulped some of the bits in an effort to stave off hunger. For a day he did so, until the limb was white for inches. He explored the twigs of the nest for insects which might be there, and his blooded eyes searched the surrounding limbs for acorns.

At long intervals he darted from the nest to snatch the few scattered acorns. They were bitter and small, and pulled his throat muscles together to make his desire for food more acute.

His breast was growing cold with his hunger, and he tried to fluff his feathers still more.

Hunger began pushing instinct back. The huge passenger flights seemed far in the past. Food had to be got now.

He waited until the next midday when the sun was warmest. Then he flew frantically to the distant hillsides which he knew to contain food. It was there, deep red sumac seeds which filled his crop, and oily ripe beechnuts which puffed it still further and eased his craving.

Perhaps he had waited too long, for he spent many minutes finding the mast. When he was through he sped back on pumping wings.

He knew, as he dropped onto the nest, that he had been away too long. The eggs were chilled, their coldness embodying the lifelessness of winter itself. Blue nudged them together beneath him and steeled himself to give warmth.

Through the hours of the afternoon, and the night that followed, and most of the next day, Blue hovered and warmed the things which could not be warmed. He began to know that the eggs were lifeless now—that with the coming of the cold had gone his kind.

Blue stood, then hopped to the naked limb and gazed for a moment at the red evening horizon. He half crouched, then sprang away to become a dot in the sky—shrinking toward the warmth which seemed to rest on the far western mountains.